Saul's eyes were slivers of ice. 'My birth may not have been covered by the legal Gorgio law of matrimony, although my mother and father married in a register office very soon afterwards. In any event, in the eyes of the Romanies I was born *in* wedlock, not outside it. Which is more than can be said for Lowenna!'

Francesca's fists clenched involuntarily in her lap. 'Keep Lowenna out of this!'

'Why? It seems to me that Lowenna is. . .pivotal to the whole sorry tale.'

'Well, perception never was your strong point.'

'Is that really how you see me now?' Saul sounded thoughtful. 'I'll tell you how *I* see things, shall I? Your version of reality was always spiced up with your romantic gypsy fantasies. Not many men could measure up to those, could they? Although there was quite a fan club trying!'

'Saul, please. . .' She shivered, suddenly frightened of the dark depths of bitterness which seemed to have been dredged up between them.

Books you will enjoy
by ROSALIE ASH

UNSAFE HARBOUR

After her father's death, Charlotte devoted herself to the salvaging of his boatyard business—only to be thwarted by co-inheritor Drew Meredith. And Drew seemed determined to remind Charlotte of her teenage crush on him—or had it been a crush? And was it all in the past?

PRIVATE PROPERTY

When Henrietta finally accepted Nick Trevelyan's wonderful job offer, she didn't need to hear his previous secretary's warning about the folly of falling in love with her dark, brooding boss. But Nick seemed bent on taking possession of her—and how much longer would she be able to resist his kisses?

THE GYPSY'S BRIDE

BY

ROSALIE ASH

MILLS & BOON LIMITED
ETON HOUSE   18–24 PARADISE ROAD
RICHMOND   SURREY   TW9 1SR

First published in Great Britain 1991 by Mills & Boon Limited

© Rosalie Ash 1991

Australian copyright 1991 Philippine copyright 1991 This edition 1991

ISBN 0 263 77188 1

Set in 10 on 12 pt Linotron Times 01-9108-52377 Typeset in Great Britain by Centracet, Cambridge Made and printed in Great Britain

CHAPTER ONE

SAUL GALLAGHER was here. Catching sight of the tall, broad-shouldered figure standing motionless on the other side of the church, next to his mother, Francesca caught her breath abruptly, her heart starting to thud so rapidly that for a few seconds she wondered if she was actually going to faint, have a 'fit of the vapours' like a tightly laced Victorian virgin.

Taking a brutal grip on her nerves, she clutched the wooden pew in front of her, mocking her own naïvety. It was obvious that Saul would turn up at her father's funeral, wasn't it? He might have found his jet-setting, polo-playing life too absorbing and enthralling to bother to visit Bellbridge for the past four years, but she and Saul went back a long way—there was no escaping that bitter reality—and, since his mother Carol had rung with sympathy and support and arranged to drive down from Warwickshire and stay overnight, whatever had made her assume that she was safe from a similar duty-visit from Saul?

The last few years seemed to be full of 'if onlys'. . .if only she could switch back the clock and rearrange those fateful moments after her eighteenth birthday party; if only her father's health hadn't suddenly trapped her at Hill Mead, stopping her from making the escape she would undoubtedly have made, binding her to the family home and family business with invisible ties too emotive to break.

And now Saul was back, to judge, criticise. . .gloat?

5

Biting her lip, she cut short her brief glance over the rapidly filling church, and jerked her head back to face the altar, shivering convulsively, glad of the thick curtain of straight dark hair which swung forward to hide her troubled blue eyes.

'Are you all right?' Sarah's concerned glance took in the whiteness of her clenched knuckles, the tense pallor of her face above the dark wool of her coat. 'You look awfully pale, Chessy. . .'

On her other side, Angus slid a supportive hand through her arm, whispering, 'Chin up, sweetheart; soon be over.'

Francesca hardly heard them. She was still inwardly railing against Saul's *uninvited* presence. How dared he come today, when he'd thoroughly despised her father and ended up telling him so in no uncertain terms? Didn't he have any idea of the insensitivity of his appearance now, at such a private time of sadness, after four years of silence?

But no, she wasn't being entirely honest, was she? What a hypocrite she was. The shock of seeing him had nothing to do with intrusion into a moment of personal grief or the feud between Saul and her father. The return of Saul Gallagher to Bellbridge stirred back to life the whole tangled burden of the past, blatant truths she'd conveniently fallen into the habit of forgetting, uncomfortable facts she'd rather die than own up to. She could only thank heaven that his appearance would merely be fleeting. Saul's glamorous career was unlikely to spare him for more than twenty-four hours at most. . .

The organ was beginning to play and more villagers were filing into the church. Francesca huddled stiffly inside her long black coat, moved to see so many people. Clive St Aubyn hadn't been popular exactly. His temper had rather precluded popularity, growing progressively worse since Mother's death. But he'd been well respected. That was what funerals were all about, weren't they? Paying your last respects. The village had grown accustomed to Clive St Aubyn and his wife and daughter living up at Hill Mead, owning and running the Hill Mead Stables. When a horse had slipped on a muddy bridleway and crushed her mother beneath it, Francesca had been only fourteen, but she could still remember the shocked turn-out of their neighbours and friends, the generous kindness and support.

But her father's death had come as no shock. She'd known for three years that he was dying. On this occasion she'd had time—time she didn't want, admittedly, but still time—to come to terms with the prospect of losing someone, time to sort through all the various stages of grief and anger that seemed to go along with it. . .

'. . .in the midst of life we are in death. . .' the vicar was intoning. Francesca met Sarah's sympathetic hazel eyes and grimaced wryly, fighting down the hard lump in her throat. She was glad that Sarah had come; since her oldest schoolfriend had married Angus McLaren, the local vet, all three had become close, almost like the brother and sister Francesca had always longed for, and never had. Sarah had been a tower of strength over the past three years. . .

She wasn't quite sure how she got through the rest of the ceremony, or how she maintained her poise as she stood at the graveside within the soft, rolling beauty of the Devon countryside rising up on either side of the ancient church. She was suddenly painfully conscious of how strange Hill Mead was going to seem without her father stamping about the place, snarling orders.

She could feel her composure cracking, and drew deep, shuddering breaths to control herself. Look at the signs of summer on its way, she ordered herself silently, gritting her teeth; look around at new beginnings; the white May blossom on the hawthorn, even a mist of bluebells up in the woods. Between massive yew trees there was a kissing-gate, leading to the footpath which wound up towards the moor. One of her favourite rides lay up there. . . She dashed an impatient hand across her eyes, forcing herself to take comfort from the idyllic setting.

Aunt Carol, just as beautiful as ever with her blue eyes and her wavy Titian hair, still with that vague hint of the bohemian in her flowing skirt and shawl, appeared at her side and hugged her tightly as the graveside mourners began to disperse.

'Hello, Francesca; it's so lovely to see you again, darling, after all this time!' Wise blue eyes scanned her stricken face shrewdly. 'You look shattered. I'm not surprised. I'm sorry I couldn't come down any earlier, my dear. You must be exhausted, having all the arrangements to make on your own. I expect you could do with some time to yourself, rather than having everyone back to Hill Mead for the traditional gathering. . .'

'No. . .' Francesca's voice was choked, but she held herself tightly in check. 'It all right, Carol, really. It's lovely to see you, too. I've missed you a lot. . . Did you have a good drive down?'

'Apart from the usual endless roadworks on the M5. And I feel quite cross that no one *told* me about Clive's illness,' her aunt murmured reprovingly. 'I knew your father had been a bit of a recluse since Ann died, and I know he and I weren't exactly on speaking terms since I sold Leigh Barton, but you really shouldn't have borne this on your shoulders, all by yourself! You should have written to me, Francesca!'

'I know. I'm sorry. Dad wouldn't let me tell anyone. I couldn't break his confidence, Carol. It was his life, after all. His choice to make. . .'

'Yes,' the older woman sighed, pushing back a bright wisp of hair barely tinged with grey despite Carol's being in her late forties, her eyes rueful. 'Though I hate the thought of being on bad terms with him; now he's dead and we can never resolve the argument. But, still, it wasn't just selling Leigh Barton that upset him. Let's face it, your father could never quite get used to the thought of his brother marrying me in the first place.' Aunt Carol waved her hand at Francesca's protest with a sad smile. 'No, don't say it. I'm a philosophical person, Francesca, and I assure you I bear your father no grudges. I've been quite happy, immersed in my lecturing, with the occasional phone call from Saul in some exotic far-off place. I've been guilty of becoming a bit of a recluse myself!'

Just as well, Francesca told herself silently, feeling panic ebbing and flowing inside her as the inevitable revelation loomed closer and closer. They were moving slowly down towards the lych-gate as they talked, and Carol was glancing round the various groups of friends and relatives, trying to see where Saul was, Francesca knew. Where *was* Saul? She'd last seen him standing with his mother at the graveside, and she'd deliberately avoided the level, piercing gaze directed at her above the heads of most of the people in front of him.

Unconsciously quickening her pace, she parted from

Saul's mother at her smart little banana-yellow Metro, and went in search of her mud-splashed Land Rover further along the narrow lane, to find it hemmed in at both ends. A large, shiny green Range Rover was blocking the front, and a slightly battered blue Ford Sierra, which she recognised immediately as the vicar's, was tightly wedged in behind.

Impatience and frustration welled up. It was imperative that she get back to Hill Mead before Aunt Carol, and before Saul for that matter, assuming that he'd be calmly attending the funeral party with his mother.

With a fruitless glance around for the owner of the Range Rover, she began to make her way rapidly back up to the church to ask the vicar to move his car, and in her haste nearly collided with Saul as he emerged from the shadow of the lych-gate.

'Hello, Chessy. Where are you tearing off to?'

The deep voice, with its flat, public-school drawl, was so achingly familiar that she realised that she'd know it blindfolded, even after all this time. He loomed in front of her, topping her own slender five feet five inches by an annoying six inches, seeming far taller than she remembered, and far darker.

'Saul.' Her smile was mainly for the benefit of one or two straggling, curious onlookers, icily polite and impersonal as she struggled to hide her reaction to his sudden closeness. 'What a pleasant surprise. What brings you back to Bellbridge? You surely haven't flown all the way from Argentina just for my father's funeral?'

Slate-grey eyes narrowed thoughtfully on her face. 'I'm very sorry about your father, Francesca,' he said at last, ignoring the calculated rudeness of her thrust.

'I've recently been told he'd been ill for a couple of years. You've had a tough time.'

'I managed,' she countered evenly. 'Life goes on.'

His mouth twisted. 'Very trite. Is that all you can say?'

She shrugged stiffly, a sense of unreality pervading her, followed rapidly by the beginning of simmering anger.

'What do you expect me to say to you?' she enquired in a frigid undertone. 'Pour my heart out, perhaps, even though we're virtually strangers?'

'Strangers?' Something in the ironic lift of Saul's dark eyebrows brought a flood of colour into her cheeks. 'Hardly, Chessy.'

Her heart lurched, and she clenched her hands into tight fists in her pockets. No, they weren't strangers. But it might be easier if they were. They weren't strangers; they were cousins—step-cousins. And until four years ago they'd shared the closeness that comes only from spending the early years of your life with someone. Saul had been the big brother she'd never had. She'd idolised him, worshipped him, been enthralled by the glamour of his background, so start-lingly different from hers. . .

No, she acknowledged bitterly. They weren't strangers. And Saul was going to find out today about Lowenna. . .but it wouldn't change anything, she told herself fiercely. It *couldn't* change anything.

Wide, gentian-blue eyes glared warily up into calcu-lating grey, and she watched the flicker of reaction as he gauged the depth of her hostility. She lifted her chin, meeting his gaze levelly. 'We may have grown up together, but everything changed four years ago.'

'We need to talk about that.' Saul's flat tone was hard to decipher.

'No!' It came out more panic-stricken than she had intended, and she flinched under his lidded scrutiny. 'There's nothing to talk about. What happened just. . .happened. I definitely don't want to talk about it.'

'You've changed,' Saul remarked after a lengthy silence. 'Maybe you've grown up at last.'

'Full marks for observation. Most people do a fair amount of growing up between the ages of eighteen and twenty-two.'

'Maybe.' Saul was inspecting her in an unnervingly detached fashion. 'Twenty-two to twenty-six have proved fairly formative years in my case.'

She avoided that penetrating gaze, aping his scrutiny by examining his appearance as calmly as she could, taking in the expensive charcoal suit, fine silk shirt and tie, impeccable quality of trenchcoat and Oxford brogues.

'Yes.' She nodded, her voice cool, her words coming involuntarily from a deep well of bitterness she hadn't even realised existed until this moment. 'At least you look as if you've finally abandoned your Romany obsession——'

'I thought you were the one with the obsession, Chessy.' The interruption was softly spoken, but there was a wary glitter in his eyes now, as if he sensed warfare and was weighing up his own position.

'All right.' She shrugged slightly. 'You've had your hair cut.' She eyed the unmistakable London cut of his wavy dark hair. 'You've made yourself bags of money as a hired assassin on the polo field, you've bought yourself a few designer suits and you've got rid of the gold earring. Presumably you're now a fully paid-up member of our much-despised Gorgio society. Am I supposed to be impressed?'

For a few seconds she thought that Saul was about to lose his temper, but then he threw her into confusion by grinning at her with that rueful charm she remembered only too well from the past.

She couldn't help staring at him, her full lower lip caught involuntarily between small white teeth as she watched the transformation wrought by that heart-catching smile.

'No, Chessy,' he said softly, 'you're not supposed to be impressed at all.'

There was a charged silence. She could feel her whole body starting to shiver with awareness under that narrowed, mocking gaze. What was it about him, she wondered distractedly, that had this disturbing effect on her? It wasn't just the potent combination of pale grey eyes and swarthy colouring; it had to be something else, something unique to Saul Gallagher's personality.

His Romany blood? The mythical romance of the gypsy, with all its colourful imagery and folklore—she winced silently at the thought; there were too many humiliating connotations from the past attached to that explanation—so maybe it was this infuriatingly *sardonic* impression of power?

That was it, she reassured herself bitterly. That was the explanation, and self-knowledge was the first step to self-protection. Saul Gallagher looked like a man who'd examined all life's difficult questions and found the answers for himself, without expending too much energy in the process. And it was a smokescreen. Nobody as callous and self-interested as Saul could possibly be as wise and powerful as she'd once so naïvely imagined him to be.

'Excuse me, I have to go and find the vicar. His car's blocking me in.' She made to pass him, but he stopped her, stretching out a hand with a curiously economical movement, detaining her without any apparent effort although she was furiously aware of the strength of his grip on her arm.

'It'll be easier if I just move my Range Rover.'

'*You* blocked me in?'

'Calm down. Parking is tight in these narrow lanes. I recognised the Hill Mead Land Rover, and I hazarded a guess we'd be leaving at around the same time.'

'Did you?' She took a deep, steadying breath, aware that she was grossly over-reacting. 'Well, it looks as if you were right, doesn't it? And, since your mother has already gone on ahead to Hill Mead, I'd better formally invite you up to the funeral party. But for heaven's sake don't feel obliged to come. I'm sure no one will mind if you head on back to the polo field without delay!'

'Do I receive a loud, clear message that my return to Bellbridge is far from welcomed, Francesca?' Saul sounded infuriatingly calm and thoughtful, nothing like as illogically goaded and furious as she felt inside, and it fuelled her anger even more.

'Let go of me. . .!' She suppressed the mounting panic, hating herself for her weakness. Out of the corner of her eye she caught a glimpse of Sarah's blonde curls blowing in the breeze. She and Angus were talking to some friends only a few yards away, and Francesca was conscious of Sarah's wide hazel eyes straying curiously in her direction.

'Surely, now that your father is no longer standing

jealous guard over your St Aubyn honour, we could manage to be civil to each other?' Saul was saying levelly.

The colour washed into her face then receded abruptly. 'Civil to each other?' she echoed bitterly. 'Yes, of course. I'm sure we can manage that. But let go of my arm, please. And, in case you'd forgotten, this is my father's funeral. Not exactly an appropriate time for snide remarks about him!'

Slowly, consideringly, he dropped her arm, and she stepped away from him, a swift glance towards her friends showing her that they'd tactfully turned away, starting to stroll down the lane to where the cars were parked. Clearly, even though they were well out of earshot, body language alone was enough to demonstrate the emotion-packed scenario taking place. Francesca flicked Saul a furious glare and set off rapidly in the direction of her car, aware that, with Saul's easy, loping stride, he had no problem in keeping up with her.

'What are your plans for the stables?' he asked quietly when she stopped by the Land Rover, his grey eyes like searchlights on her flushed face as she began to climb into the vehicle. 'Are you going to sell?'

She stared at him challengingly. 'Of course not. I've been running the stables all by myself for the last three years, since Dad became ill. . . Why on earth should I sell?'

Saul's wide mouth twisted mockingly. 'It occurred to me you might have a few financial difficulties.'

'I'll get by. I have very definite plans for Hill Mead Stables, plans I've had for some time but haven't been able to instigate because of my father's. . .my father's health.' She'd been about to say, because of her father's opposition, but stifled the admission just in time, adding decisively, 'In any case, I don't need any help or advice from you, Saul. There's absolutely nothing to keep you from jetting back to your polo and all those suntanned blondes you keep getting photographed with in the Sunday magazines!'

His eyes darkened, but there was a flicker of amusement there too. 'Why so bitter, Chessy?' he murmured, almost reflectively. 'Have I committed such an unforgivable sin in your eyes?'

She stared at him mutinously, her breathing shallow with the effort to stay calm. Saul's sin was more one of omission, she thought silently, and she was certainly not going to give him the satisfaction of explaining how much, how deeply she'd been hurt by his total indifference these last four years. When it came down to it, she had difficulty understanding it herself. His absence abroad, his total involvement in his polo career, had in many ways been exactly what she'd have chosen herself, so why did she feel so betrayed by it? It didn't make any sense at all.

'I just prefer independence.' She averted her eyes from his searching gaze. The shiny cascade of her hair caught in the wind and whipped across her face.

'Independence?' Was there a hint of gentle mockery back in Saul's voice? 'You prefer independence, yet you've stayed at Hill Mead all this time, safe in your little childhood haven, being manipulated and pushed around by your father. What happened to those grand plans of yours to do Theatre Studies at university?'

'My father became ill,' she retorted icily, scraping a lock of dark hair from her eyes with a hand which shook slightly. 'I could hardly dash off to college.

When his illness was first diagnosed, he was given six months to live! I was all he had. He needed me!'

Saul gazed at her steadily, then nodded slowly. She could see his brain skimming rapidly through available information, spotting discrepancies in her story, and she wanted to lash out and hit him for that patronising analysis.

'Yes. Your father needed you, all right,' he said at last, his tone dry, 'and he never let you forget it, did he?'

Her stomach tightened, and she slowly sat down in the driving-seat, eyeing him coldly.

'If you'll just move your car, I'll see you back at Hill Mead.' She slammed the door decisively, her eyes cool, adding through the open window, 'That's if you can remember the way.'

Saul obediently reversed the Range Rover, and since Francesca was facing in the right direction she drove off first, but the triumph of her parting shot was short-lived. As she pulled away, she was trembling so violently that she clashed the gears in an ignominious, ear-splitting screech, and in the rear-view mirror she saw Saul sitting motionless, gazing after her, as she disappeared around the bend in the lane.

The route up to Hill Mead wound through narrow, high-sided Devon lanes, the grassy green banks already spangled with red campion, and blue periwinkle, stitch-wort and violets, but Francesca was too preoccupied to notice. Parking the Land Rover alongside the usual clutter of vehicles around the stableyard—the horse-boxes and the large Bedford trunks bearing the proud legend 'Hill Mead Stables, Competition Horses'—she waved briefly to Gina supervising the students there, and ran into the house, flinging her coat on to the hook in the hall, combing her fingers through her dishevelled hair to tidy it and bracing herself for the normal exuberant welcome of Spike the spaniel's yapping combined with Lowenna's non-stop volley of chatter.

'She's upstairs, asleep, and Ellen let her take the dog with her,' Mrs Prince supplied, bustling across the hall towards the murmur of muted chatter in the sitting-room with a tray of canapés. 'She got rather over-excited, I'm afraid.'

'I know.' Francesca smiled sadly at the housekeeper. 'Lowenna's rather sensitive to atmosphere—she might be only three but she knows Grandpa's not here any more. I suspect that's why she made all that fuss about your staying with her this afternoon.'

The older woman nodded. 'Security. I didn't mind in the least, so don't look so guilty, dear! I'm not a great one for funerals. I was fond of your father, but if I was more use here, looking after the little one, that suits me fine.'

'Thanks. . .' Francesca hesitated a fraction '. . . I'm very grateful for all your help with her, you know. She's really fond of you, Mrs Prince.'

'The feeling's entirely mutual. And *you* look exhausted, my love. Go and collapse in the study. I'll bring you some tea and sandwiches. Leave your guests to me.'

Francesca was about to protest, then realised that, if she didn't go and recover alone for a few minutes, she was in danger of collapsing on her guests instead. She nodded with uncharacteristic meekness, and went into the study where an ancient wood-burning stove threw a welcoming orange glow over equally ancient leather armchairs. Pictures of horses—prints, photographs, sketches—covered the smoke-stained wallpaper. Sinking on to the window-seat, she stared unseeingly out at the green panorama of hills and fields beyond, with the dark purplish hump of the moor lurking in the far distance.

The pale green branches of the ash tree closest to the house were swaying gently in the wind. After a winter of fierce storms, May would hopefully bring a good summer, despite the chill in the evenings.

Leaning back against the window embrasure, she slid brown-booted feet up and hugged her knees, glad of the warmth of her long heather-blue tweed skirt and toning thick hand-knitted angora sweater, snugly belted at the waist. Hill Mead had been her father's inheritance from the St Aubyn family estate, with Leigh Barton and all the surrounding farmland going to his older brother Harry. It was wonderful for its views, but the flip side of the coin was the draughts which howled in virtually all year round, finding numerous easy entry points in the ill-fitting windows and doors. Hill Mead wasn't old and pretty like Leigh Barton, an ancient Devon manor-house with cosy thatch and white-rendered walls; it was just old, granite-built from the stone up on the moor, originally a pair of farmworkers' cottages which had been knocked into one and greatly added to over the years. Her father had built the stables and gradually acquired more land as his business had grown.

A photograph of her parents, taken years ago when her mother had won the National Side-Saddle Championships, stared down at her from the chimney-piece. Her mother was laughing, her eyes sparkling at the camera. Her father wore his habitual expression of remote disapproval. Francesca gazed at it thoughtfully.

Her own colouring, dark blue eyes, dark hair and olive skin, were derived from her mother; her father's iron-grey hair had once been blond, his stern, intolerant eyes rather a pale shade of green. She felt a fresh wave of unhappiness engulf her. She was grieving for her father, but suddenly she found herself longing for her mother to such a degree that she had to bite back bitter tears.

Voices in the hall brought her rapidly alert. Saul had arrived. The pleasure she could detect in Mrs Prince's greeting gave her a stab of totally unworthy irritation.

When the door opened, and Saul appeared with a tray of canapés and a bottle of red wine, she was on her feet, bristling indignantly.

'The rest of the guests are in the sitting-room,' she began coldly, as Saul calmly placed the tray on the table by the stove. 'I'd rather be left alone, Saul. . .'

'I'd have thought you'd been alone too much recently. And we must have a few things to catch up on, since we haven't seen each other for so long.' He was uncorking the bottle with casual expertise as he spoke. 'I seem to remember you like red wine.'

She glared at him, her defences annoyingly under-mined by the sight of him in the expensive dark grey suit, the play of well-honed muscles evident beneath the smooth material as he extracted the cork and set the bottle back on the tray.

He glanced up suddenly and met her eyes, his smile wry. 'You look struck dumb, Chessy.'

'I was just thinking how rarely I've seen you in a suit. You used to live in ripped Levis and leather waistcoats.' Her tone was indifferent, but she was appalled to realise that inside she felt far from indiffer-ent. That subtle magnetism she'd fought so hard to erase from her memory seemed to be infuriatingly alive and kicking. She wanted to run out of the room or scream at him to get out, but her throat seemed to have constricted and her knees refused to function.

Saul was nonchalantly tugging at the black silk tie and undoing the top button of an immaculate Jermyn Street shirt, unsettling her even more by shrugging off the jacket and slinging it across the back of a chair before he began pouring the wine.

'I still dislike suits,' he admitted wryly, straightening to hand her a glass.

Why did he hate them, she wondered distractedly, automatically accepting the wine, when they made him look as good as they did? She looked away, her throat drying even more, and took a large sip of her drink. She could see her own reflection in the mirror over the chimney-piece, her face a pale blur within a frame of tumbled dark hair.

'Well, luckily you don't have to wear them very often, do you?' she managed to say derisively. 'I imagine you spend most of your days galloping up and down in very macho white breeches and scuffed brown boots. Have you attained the coveted ten-goal handicap yet?'

'No. I'm not sure if I will.'

'Really? The talk is always about your being the rising star; at least, it is in the gossip pages you seem to get into with monotonous regularity. Or is twenty-six considered over the hill in polo?'

She was being deliberately rude, she knew, and as usual it was a form of self-defence. The awkward moment of truth could only be delayed for a regrettably short time, and the prospect of Saul's reaction was decidedly bringing out the worst in her. She had the grace to blush slightly at the level, quizzical stare he turned on her.

'There are other things in life apart from playing polo.'

'Such as?'

Saul was refusing to rise to the bait. 'What do you think of the wine?' he enquired smoothly.

'It's quite. . .pleasant.'

'It's a good one. Nuits-St-Georges Les Pruliers. That's one thing I did admire your father for—his excellent wine-cellar.'

'You didn't admire my father for anything! You detested him!'

'The feeling was mutual.'

'Saul, I don't know why you've bothered to come today, but as far as I'm concerned the sooner you go again the better. And if you've just come back to. . .to gloat. . .'

'Gloat?' The grey eyes darkened. 'What kind of a monster do you think I am, Francesca?'

'I. . . I'm sorry, maybe that was rather strong,' she said tightly.

Silence stretched between them, loaded with unspoken thoughts and emotions.

'Francesca, whatever interpretation you put on the past,' Saul said finally, his tone level, "detest" is too strong a word. Your father felt. . .threatened by me. All the hostility between us sprang from that.'

She lowered her lids, sipping the wine and striving for an unruffled calm to match Saul's. How could he be so. . .so cool and analytical?

'So let's drink to your father,' there was no trace of mockery in his eyes when she glanced abruptly up at him, 'just to prove we've both matured in the last four years.'

Saul's hard mouth twisted wryly as he raised his glass, watching her internal battles reflected in her expression.

'To the father you loved very much, Francesca. In celebration of the good times you shared.'

The down-to-earth realism of the sentiment touched her, in spite of her hostility. It had more impact than conventional comfort or sympathy. And somehow she sensed Saul's sincerity.

She stared at him again, her throat drying. In the fading afternoon light, the fire was throwing flickers of light across his face, throwing one side into deep shadow, highlighting the other into harsh angles and planes. A wavy lock of thick black hair fell slightly forward across his forehead, and he raked it back.

'Have a canapé,' he suggested quietly. 'They look like cream-cheese and prawn.'

'No. . .thanks. I'm not hungry.'

'Then have some more wine. It's medicinal.'

She choked slightly, the hint of the smile in Saul's eyes making her heart ache for a reason she preferred not to analyse.

'Medicinal? I'm not sure we should put a bottle of my father's treasured Nuits-St-Georges in the same category as. . .as cough mixture.'

The brilliant glitter of his laugh had been almost forgotten in the four years since she'd seen him. Catching her breath jerkily, she took an unladylike gulp of the wine and averted her eyes, hot tears prickling and threatening to spill down over her face.

'Francesca. . .'

The deep voice was compelling, but his tone was

unfathomable and it was impossible to tell if he was offering comfort, or something else, and she was terrified to find out. The past was suddenly too raw, too full of pain—pain he'd caused her, or pain she'd caused herself; she wasn't even sure any more.

He reached out and took her hand, and the shock of his cool grip on her fingers triggered a sort of drowning sensation, an enveloping wave of emotion so over-powering that she almost forgot past and future, simply experiencing this electrifying moment in the present.

'Chessy. . .' Saul's voice was unrecognisable, rough and urgent. He tightened his fingers and took a step closer. Afterwards she was utterly appalled by what happened in that strange, involuntary moment, but somehow, instead of recoiling in protest, she opened her palm in mute surrender, her fingers sliding between his, as if in a dream, so that their hands clasped together so tightly she could feel the vibration of his pulse-rate against the delicate pulse in her own wrist. . .

'Saul. . .' it was a choked whisper '. . . Saul, I——'

Whatever she would have said in that moment of intense emotion was abruptly curtailed by a commotion outside, with Aunt Carol's, Mrs Prince's and Ellen's voices drowned out by a small, high-pitched one, tearfully demanding, 'Mummy? Mummy! Want my mummy *now*!' The door opened abruptly to admit Ellen, the latest nineteen-year-old nanny, her rosy face even more flushed than normal, soft brown hair escap-ing its pony-tail, being forcibly towed along by an elfin figure in red kilt and yellow sweater with a picture of a bear on the front, two long dark plaits tied with red ribbons, and large, accusing grey eyes which rapidly

swept around the dimly lit room, and settled trium-
phantly on Francesca.

'Mummy!'

Francesca snatched her hand from Saul's as if she'd
been burned, turning her back on him to crouch down
with an incandescent smile of greeting to the child.

'Hello, Lowenna; come here, darling.'

And, under the stunned combined gaze of Saul and
Carol, the small figure flung itself across the study and
into Francesca's waiting arms.

CHAPTER TWO

FRANCESCA slept very badly. The day had been emotional enough with her father's funeral, but the awkward scenario afterwards back at Hill Mead had produced the worst possible combination for insomnia: an exhausted body and an over-active brain.

She tossed and turned furiously, listening to the rustle of the wind in the pine trees, growing hotter and hotter until she kicked off the continental quilt and then finally discarded her blue satin pyjamas in a heap on the floor and curled herself into a foetal position, slender, well-muscled arms wrapped defensively around the fullness of her breasts, dark hair spread out like a fan on the pillow.

Her stomach felt knotted with tension. It was impossible to relax. After four long years, Saul was sleeping in the guest room just across the landing, biding a dangerous, explosive silence on the subject of Lowenna. . . She shuddered at the prospect of Saul's reaction, all the more daunting because of his absence of comment so far. Tomorrow would bring the inevitable interrogation, she knew. She had it all to come. The only reason she'd been spared last night was a mixture of his own iron self-control and Aunt Carol's mediating influence.

The trouble was, she knew him too well. He might be arrogant and chauvinistic, but he wouldn't spark off a major row in front of a three-year-old child. But the fact that he'd calmly accepted Mrs Prince's offer of a bed for the night, instead of high-tailing it off to his polo yard in Berkshire again, was ominous in itself.

She shivered, and pulled her quilt back up to cover herself, her thoughts twisting in another direction. Wasn't she assuming too much about Saul's reaction? It suddenly occured to her that her long-ago decision *not* to tell him about Lowenna might have fostered all kinds of fantasies about his reactions if he knew, about his feelings towards her.

Saul had hardly proved himself a devoted step-cousin recently, had he? He hadn't shown a scrap of interest in her life for four years, and before that he'd said some cruel, brutal things to her, things she'd never forget as long as she lived.

Face it: wasn't it far more likely that he'd be fairly *indifferent* to the whole thing? That thought both comforted and tortured, and with a groan she rolled on to her stomach, burying her head in the pillow and trying to calm her confused thoughts.

The trouble was that the past, in itself, was confusing. Nothing had ever seemed to happen calmly and rationally between herself and Saul. It had always been love-hate. There had always been an ambiguous air of competition between them. And her persistent hero-worship for Saul had always been tempered by her father's contempt. She'd seen Saul as exciting, different, blessed with almost magical powers and innate wisdom. As a child, he'd been big brother, friend, cousin, all rolled into one. She'd adored Saul's mother, Aunt Carol, with her exuberant sense of fun, her off-beat attitudes, and been devastated when she moved away just after Mother died.

Her father, conversely, had viewed Saul with suspicion, as an unwelcome infiltrator into their family.

He'd despised Carol for having been foolish enough to not only get pregnant during a madly romantic affair with a high-born Romany travelling through her home town, but for actually being rash enough to become the gypsy's bride as well. The fact that she was highly intelligent—a graduate social anthropologist doing a thesis on the Romany lifestyle when she met and married her gypsy lover—merely compounded the stupidity. That the ill-matched marriage failed was no surprise in his eyes, but for his respected elder brother Harry to marry a woman with a one-year-old baby, and whose previous marriage had been, according to her father, merely a private Romany ceremony without the legality of the law of the land, was the final straw for Clive St Aubyn. If she'd heard his opinion once she must have heard it a thousand times.

How he'd hated her closeness to Saul; 'the gypsy invader', he'd called him.

It was Aunt Carol she felt really guilty about. Not telling Saul had been an automatic, reflex decision. Not telling her aunt had been unavoidable, but very painful. In order to ensure that Saul hadn't found out, come barging back to Hill Mead with questions and judgements and arrogant interference, she'd been prevented from telling the one person in the world she'd longed to tell most of all, the person whose tolerance and sheer *earthiness* could have helped her through so much.

And the pain must have worked both ways, Francesca thought miserably, thinking of the older woman's expression during dinner last night. Francesca opened her eyes and stared unseeingly at the mauve flowered curtains billowing in the draught through the window-frame. Her aunt was deeply hurt, but too considerate to show it. And there was still so much left unsaid. . .

Last night, when the rest of the guests had gone and Lowenna was safely in bed, the three of them had sat down to dinner and, while Saul had remained taciturn, his thoughts and feelings completely unreadable, she and Carol had made polite, wary conversation about coping with small children alone, the logistics of being a single working parent, and so on. But, with Saul's ominous calm and scant contribution to the discussion, it had seemed impossible to say the things she wanted to say. When her aunt had announced that she was off to bed, Francesca had made a cowardly dash for her own room at the same time, so keen to avoid Saul that she'd contented herself with the briefest of 'goodnight's to Carol before locking herself away in her room.

It was the longest night of her life, even worse than those endless nights when she'd longed for some word from Saul to show how he felt, yearned for the tele-phone call, or the letter that never came.

The minutes seemed to stretch into hours, with her tired brain alternately justifying, analysing, reasoning and panicking. She wasn't sure if she finally slept for a short while or not, but when the carriage clock by her bed read five-thirty a.m. she abandoned the effort and, after a quiet peep into Lowenna's room when she checked that the small sleeping figure was still warmly tucked beneath her Paddington Bear quilt, she hur-riedly showered, plaited her hair in a long rope down her back, and flung on breeches and scarlet sweater. Creeping past the guest room with her heart in her mouth, she made for the stables, snatching boots and an ancient tweed jacket as she went, hardly pausing in

her haste to escape from the house before Saul or his
mother woke up.

Vengeance's loose-box was dark and warm, and
Francesca inhaled the musky smell of horse and hay,
too preoccupied, as she groomed and fed and saddled
him, to talk to him, only acknowledging her mistake
when the horse gave her a sharp kick on the shin.

'Behave yourself—don't kick the person who feeds
you!' she advised him reproachfully, collecting her hat
from the tack-room and jamming it firmly on her head
before leading Vengeance quietly out into the deserted
yard. The horse was one of her father's very last
acquisitions before he'd become too ill to work at all,
a six-year-old Cleveland Bay gelding he'd bought
almost wild from a farmer up in Dorset. He was an
enormous horse, over sixteen hands, with powerful
hindquarters and hocks, and had an unpredictable
nature, but his wild streak rather appealed to her. With
patient schooling, hopefully he'd become a superb
show-jumper.

There was an audible whickering and stamping from
the other loose-boxes. They'd all have to wait,
Francesca reflected, rapidly urging Vengeance out on
to the lane. She didn't want Kelly, a particularly highly-
strung mare, to start kicking her water-bucket around
in frustration, unsettling all the others. The students
would be arriving at seven-thirty a.m. with Gina hot
on their heels, and the first pupils began arriving later
still—any time from nine-thirty a.m. on.

She urged the young horse up the lane and on to the
bridleway towards the wood, keeping him on a close
rein to remind him of what was expected of him, and
then relenting, giving him his head up the gradual
incline of the field, feeling him take off like a bullet

from a gun, his mane streaming in the wind while exhilaration filled her lungs with cool air.

The strong wind cleared her head as they galloped across the moor, watching the morning sky change and lighten. She rode right across to Barton Combe, then turned back to skirt her own boundaries and inspect the stretch of land she hoped to buy. It was a twenty-acre field, bordering her land and that of Leigh Barton, sheltering down there in its cosy hollow.

Halting Vengeance on the brow of the hill, she looked down at the soft lines of the house in the valley. The mellow, honey-gold of its brand-new thatch gave it a luxurious air, emphasised by the royal 'E' shape of the buildings, fashioned centuries ago by one of Elizabeth the First's courtiers as a mark of loyalty to the Crown. Francesca had always loved Leigh Barton. She hadn't been furious, as her father had, when Aunt Carol had opted to sell when Uncle Harry died, but she'd been sad. It had been Saul's house. And even if Saul had already left home, gone away to university, it had meant that he'd have no base in Devon to return to during his vacations. . .it had meant that she'd hardly ever see him. . .

The overheads were too high, Carol had explained ruefully, and anyway, it was far too big for her on her own, with Saul away. Carol was one of the most unpretentious people she knew. It had been quite easy to believe her when she'd disclaimed any desire to play the widowed 'Lady of the Manor'. But deep down, although she'd always shrunk from admitting it to herself, Francesca suspected that Carol had moved away because of Dad. Without Uncle Harry to act as a buffer between herself and her brother-in-law, Carol must have felt under subtle attack from Dad's disapproval.

Francesca remembered that as a painful phase. She'd been fourteen, secure and content, combining a love for riding, and an enthusiasm for competing in the junior show-jumping events at all the local shows, with a feeling that life held all kinds of fascinating experiences outside the boundaries of her home environment, and achievements unconnected with horses or the family stables. She'd hung on every word of wisdom dropped laconically from Saul's lips, who'd always seen life on a global scale, shown an amused contempt for what he termed 'Gorgio parochialism'. 'Gorgio' was the word the gypsies used for the rest of the human population unlucky enough not to have Romany blood in their veins. It meant peasant, yokel, bumpkin. The Romanies, he'd once told her, considered themselves to be the lords of the earth. How *arrogant* he'd always been, she recalled with a stab of bitter amusement. It had always been debatable who was the most intolerant—her father or Saul Gallagher.

But they seemed like happy times now. Abruptly her world had fallen apart when she was fourteen. Without warning, everyone she loved and cared about most had been deserting her. Her mother's death, Uncle Harry's heart attack, Saul's and Aunt Carol's departure. . . It had all happened in rapid succession.

She gazed down the hill for a long time, remembering long-ago visits, climbing trees in the apple orchard, racing ponies along the wide stretch of moor encircling the house, games of hide-and-seek in the dusty attics, treasure hunts during birthday parties. The house had changed hands twice since Aunt Carol sold up, the latter owner a man from Birmingham who wanted a show-piece Devon country estate to entertain friends and business colleagues at weekends. Unfortunately his company had gone bankrupt, and Leigh Barton had been sold again recently. Who was the rich new owner, she wondered idly, who'd made such comprehensive improvements over the last couple of months, paid for the new thatch and the repairs to the outbuildings and courtyards, yet whose identity was still frustratedly eluding the gossips in the village post office and stores? The latest rumour was that a stunning ash-blonde woman had been seen arriving and leaving, driving a big Daihatsu four-wheel drive and wielding a car-phone with a high-powered executive air about her. It would be interesting to see. . .

As a child, she'd dreamed of living there, she reflected wryly, envied Saul his home, tucked away out of the fierce winter gales which swept the south-west peninsular, with thick walls and massive inglenooks for extra security.

Vengeance was getting restless, noisily chewing his bit and shying at a flock of rooks rising up like blackened scraps of burnt paper in the wind. But she stared down the valley for a few moments longer, memories jostling for position in her mind, gazing through the fragile spring-green of the trees at Saul's old house.

By the time she cantered back towards Hill Mead she might not have solved any of her personal problems, but at least she felt calmer, she decided. And the fresh air, and the challenge of controlling Vengeance, even putting him at some easy jumps on the way back, had made her wide awake and just a fraction more confident at the daunting thought of facing Saul over breakfast.

* * *

Breakfast was in full swing as she pushed open the door of the big pine kitchen. The scene was so peacefully domesticated that she stood motionless for a few seconds, flushed and windswept, unsure of her own reactions. Lowenna was on her high-stool, her dark plait a small replica of Francesca's own, clad in workmanlike jeans and a red jumper with brown and white horses knitted in rows along front and back.

She was solemnly absorbed in conversation with Saul, who was casual in checked shirt, Aran sweater and denims, unperturbably eating toast and marmalade and drinking coffee at the large scrubbed table as if he breakfasted every morning at Hill Mead with a mystery three-year-old for company.

Ellen, looking unusually glamorous this morning in a tight black sweater-dress, finishing well short of the knee, brown hair Carmen-rollered into waves, looked star-struck, hanging misty-eyed on every word Saul uttered.

'Morning,' Francesca murmured at last, dropping a kiss on top of her daughter's head and fending off Spike's strenuous licks of greeting, her wary glance at Saul receiving no answering clues as to his mood. 'Sorry to be such a rotten hostess. Did you find everything you wanted for breakfast? There are cereals and yogurts, if you prefer. . .'

'Ellen burnt the toast twice, but Saul made it just how I like it,' Lowenna informed her seriously, to the young nanny's obvious mortification.

'Sorry,' the girl murmured, blushing, 'I kept getting side-tracked.'

I'll bet, thought Francesca to herself, watching Ellen soulfully trying to catch Saul's eyes, and turning abruptly to switch on the kettle and push more bread into the toaster, since toast seemed to be exclusively on everyone else's breakfast menu this morning. 'Don't worry, burnt toast is the least of our worries. Where's Carol, by the way?'

'My mother took tea and toast back to her room.'

Francesca swung round, suffused with fresh guilt. 'Is she not feeling well?'

'She's fine. She didn't sleep too well.'

'Oh.'

Saul stretched casually, his lidded gaze decidedly challenging as he eyed her across the sunny kitchen. 'If it comes to that, I've had better nights,' he added evenly.

'Weren't you comfortable?'

'I had things on my mind.'

There was a taut silence. Francesca averted her eyes, glancing swiftly at the clock. 'Time to go up and clean your teeth, Wenna. It's playgroup this morning.'

The child obligingly slid off her stool and then hesitated, looking at Saul enquiringly. 'Will you still be here when I get back? I want to show you how I can ride Cobber all by myself!'

Saul flicked a glance at Francesca, and nodded slowly. 'I'll be here.'

'Great!' With an excited skip, Lowenna darted out, followed by Ellen, and the silence returned, hanging heavily over the room, broken only by Spike's inelegant slurps as he drank noisily from his water bowl.

'Pity dog-training classes don't cover table manners as well as "sit", "lie" and "come".' She spoke lightly, striving to cover the irregular thump of her heart at the tumultuous tension being generated by Saul's motionless figure at the table. 'Would you like some more coffee?'

'No, thanks.'

'More toast, if I guarantee not to burn it?'

'No. . .'

'In that case, I'll take a fresh cup of tea up to Carol, if you'll excuse me.'

'Stay here, Francesca. We have to talk.'

'If it's about the stables, I'm quite happy working alone——'

'It strikes me you're happier doing everything alone.' The remark was coldly sardonic. 'Or do you just absent-mindedly forget to wear a wedding-ring? Are you going to produce a husband this morning, like a rabbit from a hat?'

She looked at him in silence, her throat drying. The yellow flowers on the wallpaper blurred out of focus as she swung away, evading his challenging stare.

'Don't you dare start moralising to me!' she said at last. 'We have nothing to talk about, Saul. This is *my* life, and I'm living it *my* way.'

'You know damn well what we have to talk about, Chessy. Or is Lowenna's existence such a sideline you don't even think she's worth discussing? Are you such a selfish little bitch that you put your horses and your stables before your child?'

The colour drained from Francesca's face, and she balled her fists in abrupt fury. 'That's not even worth answering, Saul,' she said tautly, 'but, for what it's worth, the world has moved on regarding the subject of equal rights for men and women, you know. I refuse to be made to feel *guilty* for being a single parent with a living to earn. And as for doing things alone, I've done what I felt was best for Lowenna. I feel very strongly that children need two parents. But it just depends *who* the parents are!'

Saul was regarding her very intently. There was an ominous glitter in the ice-grey eyes boring into hers, and she had to fight to keep her gaze level with his.

'And Lowenna's father didn't come up to scratch?' he suggested softly.

Francesca swung away, staring out of the window at the sweeping view, feeling as if every nerve in her body were under attack.

'Lowenna's father wasn't interested in. . .in a permanent relationship.'

'So you do know who he is?'

'Of course I know who he is.' She turned round jerkily, blue eyes smoky with anger. 'That's a foul thing to say, Saul.'

He shrugged calmly. 'I'm just recalling the situation. There were several ardent young suitors around, last time I was in Bellbridge. Sometimes these things must be quite difficult to sort out.'

There was a measured pause. Controlling her breathing with difficulty, she drew herself up to her full height, facing Saul with a smouldering look.

'What makes you think you've the right to talk to me like this?' she asked huskily. 'We may have spent some time together as children, Saul, but you're nothing to me now, and I'm nothing to you! You're neither my. . .my *brother*, nor my *guardian*, nor even my real *cousin*. As for a friend—friends don't disappear for four years at a time without even bothering with Christmas cards. How dare you come back to Bellbridge and start lecturing me?'

'I wasn't intending to lecture you. But I think I'm entitled to ask a few questions——'

'You're not entitled to anything.'

'Was it your father's idea not to tell either me or my

mother about the child?' he countered softly, his eyes dark but somehow remote, as if he was weighing something up silently and giving no clues as to his decision.

'What on earth do you mean?'

'It occurred to me it might have been a deliberate snub,' he went on reflectively, 'to keep "that bloody gypsy" and his mother out of St Aubyn business. As a method of revenge, it has a certain cruel refinement about it, Francesca.'

'You're talking rubbish. You make it sound as if I was right under my father's thumb.'

'Weren't you?'

'No!' She was scarlet in the face now, almost shaking with anger. 'You may find this hard to believe for some reason, Saul, but I have a mind of my own. I make my own decisions——'

'Then why didn't you tell me?'

'I chose not to tell you.'

'Why?'

'Because you weren't *here*,' she exploded furiously, 'and because it was *my* business and no one else's!'

'How the hell can it be *your* business, and no one else's? It takes two to make a baby, Chessy.' The deep voice was lethally soft, the expression in Saul's grey eyes so quietly formidable that she felt her stomach contract in sudden fear. She wanted to hit out at him, throw something at him—anything to jolt that arrogant, implacable scrutiny.

Before Francesca could retort, Lowenna came running into the kitchen again, face washed and anorak on, with the golden spaniel close at her heels. 'I'm all ready. Why were you shouting?'

'I wasn't shouting, I was just talking loudly,'

Francesca said quickly, giving the child a bear-hug as Ellen appeared behind her. 'Have a lovely time at playgroup, sweetheart. And if Ellen tells me you've been really good you can ride Cobber when you get back.'

'I'll be *really* good!'

Francesca felt her throat constrict as she kissed the small olive face upturned to hers. Watching them climb into Ellen's Mini, and waving from the window as the small blue car disappeared down the track to the road, she found her heart aching almost unbearably with the love she felt for her tiny daughter.

Saul was standing behind her when she turned round. His sheer size was intimidating.

'Why did you call her Lowenna?' he asked evenly, his eyes still shuttered, bright slits of grey steel narrowed on her face.

'I like the name,' she retorted shortly, side-stepping to try to widen the distance between them. 'It's Cornish. It means "joy".'

'"Joy"?' He sounded thoughtful. 'Does that reflect your feelings about the happy event, Francesca? The father presumably brought you sorrow, but his child brought you joy?'

'Lowenna is my child. I can't imagine life without her. I love her more than anyone or anything in the world.'

'And yet you let the dreamy Ellen drive her to playgroup every morning?'

She was sure she would explode inside. 'Ellen is perfectly good at her job when she's not being *chatted-up* by glamorous polo players!' she snapped. 'I need a nanny for Lowenna. I have no choice. Gina and I are teaching most of the morning; we enter students and pupils for at least one show a month. I've got nearly seventy horses here, Saul, and, though I'm negotiating for some more land at the moment, I've only got thirty acres. That's a lot of juggling around, and a lot of hay-buying. This business isn't a neat little sideline I can fit in around playing house and running up dungarees on the sewing-machine!'

'I was not "chatting-up" your nanny,' Saul protested blandly, 'I was talking to your highly entertaining little daughter while your nanny appeared to be handicapped by two left feet and a severe speech impediment——'

'Don't be so rude! I expect the poor girl was just bowled over by your rugged gypsy charm!' Francesca snapped scathingly, indignant at his teasing mockery.

'OK, calm down.' His crooked smile did appalling things to her insides, even through the haze of anger. 'Let's forget your nanny for the moment. I think I'm beginning to get the picture. You're not just playing at running a riding stables; you're high-powered, the real thing.'

'Don't be so bloody patronising.'

'Language! With small impressionable ears around, moderation must be the order of the day, surely?'

Since they'd both waved Lowenna off down the drive a few moments earlier, she decided that this gibe didn't even merit an answer. Drawing a deep breath, she began to make a fresh pot of tea, relieved to see Mrs Prince puffing up the lane on her bicycle.

'I'm going up to see your mother, Saul,' she said coolly, making her way towards the door with a tray of tea. 'Perhaps you'd be good enough to let Mrs Prince know how long you intend making use of my spare room in the meantime? While I'm normally fairly hospitable——'

'Very true.'

His inflexion was sufficiently meaningful to be deeply insulting, and she flushed, glaring at him with suppressed loathing.

'—*uninvited* guests make a lot of extra work. I'm sure you'll appreciate that.'

'Of course. If I strip my own bed, hoover the room and scrub out the *en-suite* loo, will I be redeemed?'

'Don't be so silly!'

Saul was blocking her exit into the hall, his expression managing to be both mocking and intimidating at the same time.

'Let me pass, please.'

'In a moment. If I'm being summarily dismissed from Hill Mead this morning, I'm anxious to make the most of this intimate little breakfast chat together.'

The brilliant grey eyes were narrowed assessingly on her, roaming comprehensively over the dishevelled dark hair absconding from its long plait, the tinge of angry colour in the pale olive of her skin, the agitation of her breathing as her full breasts rose and fell beneath the red polo-neck sweater. Her eyes had darkened to an angry purple under that chilling grey stare.

As if he were actually touching her she felt his probing gaze along the slender curve of her thighs in the tight breeches, the flat muscle of her stomach unchanged by pregnancy or childbirth, finally returning with infuriating calm to her parted lips. She compressed her mouth into a tight line, and tried to ignore the shivers running down her spine.

'Stop staring at me like that. . .' she began hoarsely, that drowning feeling beginning to claim her again. They both turned abruptly as the kitchen door swung open on a gust of wind, and Mrs Prince hurried in, her round face bright, her eyes on Saul.

'Good morning!' She busied herself in taking off her coat and hanging it on the back of the door before turning round with avid curiosity in her eyes. 'I've just been talking to Maggie French in the village stores. Honestly, gossip is all that woman lives on. Do you know what she told me this morning? That she thinks *you've* bought Leigh Barton back, Mr Gallagher!'

Saul had stepped back to calmly open the door for Francesca, who stayed exactly where she was, as if frozen to the spot, clutching the tray of tea in front of her like a shield. 'That's the stupidest rumour Maggie French has ever started!' She laughed shortly, then suddenly glimpsed the expression in Saul's eyes and caught her lip jerkily between her teeth.

'Well, as a matter of fact. . .' Saul began calmly, the mocking gleam clearly visible now.

'Is it *true*?' she asked faintly, staring at Saul in numb dismay.

'Yes, it is,' he said quietly, catching the horror in Francesca's blue eyes with a quirk of wry amusement.

'*You've* bought Leigh Barton?'

'Is that so difficult to believe?'

'Oh, not financially. The whole world must know you're loaded with money these days,' she said, icily polite in deference to Mrs Prince's presence. 'Politically, though, it strikes me as rather an odd move. Excuse me, I must take this up to Carol. . .'

Saul followed her into the hall, closing the kitchen door after him. 'So I don't qualify for a big welcome home, Chessy?' he taunted softly.

'What do *you* think?' She stared at him coldly. 'I suppose acquiring properties, like Monopoly cards, is *de rigueur* for people in your elevated position,' she went on thoughtfully after a longish pause. 'You've got your huge place in Berkshire, haven't you, where you stable all your polo ponies? And somewhere in the South of France, and some fancy ranch in Spain? So why not add an Elizabethan farmhouse in Devon to the list?'

'Why not indeed?'

'And in the process regain your rightful inheritance, and proclaim to the world that the gypsy misfit has finally made it to the top?'

There was an icy silence following this. Saul's eyes darkened; his jaw tightened slightly. She'd hurt him, she registered with an odd stab of pain and triumph which gave her no pleasure whatsoever.

'It's a pity, though,' she added, forcing her knees to start functioning sufficiently to carry her towards the stairs before the tea was a stone-cold offering for its intended recipient, 'if this was designed as ultimate revenge on my father. Since he's dead, you'll be denied the satisfaction of flaunting your proud ownership in his face!'

'Credit me a little more maturity than that,' Saul cut in quietly, his expression shuttered now, his eyes unreadable. 'It strikes me that you're the one bearing grudges, Francesca. Not me.'

She turned away, trying to contain her emotions. 'Anyway, it's such a beautiful family home——' Her voice was annoyingly choked. She was being foul and shamelessly insulting. But she couldn't help herself. 'I was rather hoping someone would come and really *live* in it again, not just treat it as a fancy possession to visit three times a year and leave empty for the rest!'

'I think you misunderstand me,' Saul countered

evenly, following her to the foot of the stairs, his gaze level. 'I've no intention of dividing my time between my string of "luxury residences", as you seem to so fondly imagine. I've bought Leigh Barton to live in. I intend to come and live there, full time.'

'But. . .what about your polo?' Her heart was thudding so hard now that she thought she might drop the tray.

'What about it?' His voice was dangerously soft. 'My polo is hardly likely to suffer because my yard is based in Devon rather than in Berkshire. Besides, as I said yesterday, there's more to life than playing in every polo tournament there is, Francesca.'

His gaze was penetrating as he watched her reactions, adding with chilling lack of emphasis, 'So we can look forward to seeing quite a lot more of each other in future. We'll be neighbours. Just like the old days.'

The cruel glitter in the grey eyes was unbearable. She turned away.

'Yes. Just like the old days,' she echoed with a bitter parody of enthusiasm Saul couldn't fail to notice. She marched abruptly upstairs to see Carol, her back rigid, conscious of his eyes following her.

Just like the old days. Saul's words had been deliberately mocking. It could never be that. The old days were well and truly dead, killed off four years ago when she'd been searching for something beyond her childhood closeness to Saul, something much more powerful and elusive, and Saul had made his feelings in that direction cruelly clear. She'd risked spreading her tender dreams under his feet one night, and he'd trampled deliberately all over them. . .

Angry desolation swept over her so intensely, it took

all her considerable reserves of will-power to tap on the door of her aunt's room and calmly take in the tray of tea, instead of dashing for the safe haven of her own room and sobbing her heart out in private.

CHAPTER THREE

'IF YOU really want to know how I feel,' Carol declared
calmly, leaning back against her pillows and taking a
delicate sip of tea, 'I'm absolutely thrilled to bits to
have a great-niece sprung on me out of the blue! I
intend to thoroughly spoil her, visit her whenever you'll
have me, and generally make up for lost time any way
I can.'

'Oh, Carol. . .' There were tears in Francesca's eyes,
and the older woman put down her cup and took one
clenched brown fist firmly between her own smoothly
elegant hands.

'Francesca, will you stop looking so guilt-stricken?
Of course I'm cross you didn't tell me, but you had
your reasons. You've your father's stubbornness, I
expect.'

'I'm sorry, truly. If you knew how much I wanted to
tell you more than anyone, but. . .' Francesca's voice
tailed off, as Saul's mother nodded thoughtfully.

'But you didn't want Saul to find out,' she finished
up, matter-of-factly.

Colour suffused Francesca's face, and Carol smiled
calmly.

'Don't look so panicky, Chessy, my dear. I've no
intention of interfering. It's your life.'

Francesca gazed gratefully at her aunt, wishing she
had the same happy knack of doing and saying exactly
the right thing. That was a skill that had so far eluded
her completely.

'I'm not going to judge you,' Carol added. 'Don't forget, my own life has hardly been. . .conventional.' The older woman's blue eyes were wry as she inspected Francesca's flushed cheeks. 'I do understand, and I sympathise. You're twenty-two, roughly the same age I was when my relationship with Saul's real father broke up. I was left all on my own with a small child to care for. I was lucky. I met Harry. But it's a long, lonely journey on your own.'

'I've got lots of support,' Francesca returned quietly, getting up from her seat on Carol's bed with a slight smile. 'I've been lucky too. Sarah and Angus are Lowenna's godparents. They've been marvellous. And Gina's wonderful at deputising at the stables. And then there's Mrs Prince. . .'

'Yes. You're not as high and dry as some young unmarried mothers.'

Francesca winced slightly. 'Must you use that particular phrase? "Young unmarried mothers" sounds dreadful. It has a sort of irresponsible ring to it, somehow.'

'Yes—I know what you mean. Sorry, love!'

Francesca took a deep breath, and raked a wisp of dark hair from her eyes, gazing at Saul's mother with affection. Carol St Aubyn was still relatively young, she knew, bearing in mind that she had a son of twenty-six. She'd be late forties, fifty at most. And she was still a very beautiful woman, despite her lack of affectation or make-up: tall and willowy, the glory of that curly Titian hair habitually restrained in a neat French plait at the back, and wrinkles of maturity on her warm, mobile face; but somehow the bone-structure retained the beauty of youth—probably always would.

She could never admire Carol's beauty without

thinking of that long-ago romance with her high-born Romany chief. It had always fired her imagination, even when she was a child. Carol's version was now deliberately prosaic, but Francesca had always been entranced by the sheer romance of the gypsy connection. For years, during Saul's quest for knowledge, she'd tagged along with him, eager to see and learn and be part of his mysterious heritage. She winced slightly, remembering their last, violent row, the taunting accusations Saul had flung at her. . .

'You look a long way away, Chessy, darling.'

'I was just thinking. . .about. . .about finding I was pregnant. I suppose I was lucky to have a secure place to stay. My father wasn't exactly overjoyed, but at least he didn't throw me out!'

'No.' Carol glanced at her curiously, draining her teacup. 'How *did* your father react, Chessy?'

'Badly.'

Francesca found that she didn't want to talk about her father's reaction to her pregnancy, or the following fraught months. Not even to Carol.

'Are you sure I can't get you some more toast or anything?' she asked quickly, changing the subject.

'Heavens, no. I don't need waiting on. The only reason I came back to bed with my breakfast was to leave you and Saul to talk undisturbed. The atmosphere last night could definitely have been cut with a knife! It occurred to me that discretion was the better course of action this morning.'

There was a silence.

'Did you know he was buying Leigh Barton?' Francesca tried very hard not to let an accusing note creep into her voice, but the response was a rueful smile.

'Oh, I knew. Only a few weeks ago, mind you.'

Francesca digested this, dark eyebrows drawing together in growing anger and confusion.

'Yet he didn't bother to tell me?' She twisted her hands angrily behind her back, aware that she was treading on very uncertain ground now. '*You* didn't tell me?'

Carol sighed, pulling her velvet robe around her and preparing to get out of bed. 'Saul preferred to keep his plans under wraps. Don't ask me why, my dear. As far as I'm concerned, the games you two are playing are strictly between yourselves.'

'Whatever do you mean, the games we're playing?'

Carol swung out of bed, slid her feet into brocade mules and eyed her thoughtfully. 'Chessy, love, I may have been out of touch, buried in my lecturing up in Warwickshire, but it would take a very self-absorbed person not to be aware of the undercurrents between you and Saul. You were thick as thieves as children. Now you're both acting like a couple of paranoids with persecution mania. It's nothing to do with me. I'm going to have a shower,' Carol finished up cheerfully, ignoring Francesca's white face and fierce frown. 'I want to be fully dressed and raring to go when that gorgeous little daughter of yours gets back from her playgroup this morning!'

With a quick glance at her watch, Francesca suddenly realised how late it was getting. 'I must run! I've got lessons to take this morning. I'll see you later, Carol. And. . .thanks.' She gave the older woman an impulsive hug and kissed her smooth cheek. 'I've really missed you, you know. You'll come often now, won't you?'

'Try keeping me away.' Carol disappeared into the

bathroom with a parting smile over her shoulder, Francesca flew down the stairs, through the kitchen and out to the stables, only pausing long enough to grab the half-eaten slice of toast she'd left on a plate at breakfast and which Mrs Prince had thoughtfully kept to one side. There was no sign of Saul. With any luck he'd have taken himself off to Leigh Barton to officially claim ownership. Maybe he'd drop in at the village stores on his way, congratulate Maggie on her impeccable facility for relaying everyone else's business. . .

The May sun was now brilliant in a cloudless blue sky, but the wind still blew strongly, rippling the young green wheat in the distant fields. The stableyard was a hive of activity, three of the YTS students mucking out, another two preparing the feeds. Francesca's heart plummeted as she rounded the corner and approached the office. Gina was perched on the edge of the desk, laughing and chatting with Saul. Both held mugs of coffee.

'Hi, there. The nine-thirty lesson was cancelled,' the other girl announced cheerfully. 'Lucinda Melville's got chickenpox. So I'm rubbing shoulders with the rich and famous.'

'It's the Caxford Hall Show this weekend.' She heard the coldness in her voice and knew she was risking being thought autocratic. 'There are the novices to be worked. Vengeance needs some intensive schooling. I'm taking him along for a bit of experience.'

'Vengeance? Are you serious?'

'Quite serious. He was behaving himself reasonably well when I took him out this morning.'

Gina had stood up, her pink and white face slightly more flushed than normal. Francesca wondered what was different about her, then, on closer inspection, she realised. Gina, normally shiny-faced with her long brown hair scragged anyhow into a ponytail, had carefully applied green eyeshadow, blusher, foundation, and a subtle curve of rust lipstick to her mouth, and wore her hair pinned back in a roll from her forehead and falling in a lustrous series of rippling waves down her back. The transformation was electrifying. First Ellen, now Gina, Francesca reflected in growing exasperation. Was every female at Hill Mead doomed to have her head turned by the illustrious presence of the great Saul Gallagher?

She thrust her hands impatiently into the pockets of her jacket. 'Are you still here?' she enquired shortly, glaring at Saul, who was leaning nonchalantly against the door-jamb, his lidded gaze missing nothing.

'As you can see.'

'Gina, would you mind keeping an eye on the two new students from the agricultural college? They need a lot more basic cross-country practice if they're putting in for their stages one and two next time.'

'Right. I'll go and sort them out.' With a wistful glance back at Saul, Gina marched off to carry out orders, leaving a wary silence behind her in the office.

'She seems very capable. Is she well qualified?'

'Of course. She's a fully qualified instructor, and she's got her certificate in stable management too. I don't know what I'd do without Gina.'

'How about you? Have you managed to fit in all your examinations along with having babies and running riding stables and nursing sick relatives, Chessy?'

'I've got my Intermediate Instructor,' she answered tightly, turning away from Saul's disturbing presence to scan the diary for the day. 'After that, as you so rightly say, life got a bit hectic.'

'So, when do you relax?'

'When I fall into bed at night?' she suggested acidly, instantly wishing she hadn't used that particular instance as she watched the wry gleam in his eyes.

'Come and have a meal with me tonight.'

'I'm sorry, I couldn't possibly spare the time.'

'There's a new restaurant opened up in the Cathedral Square in Exeter. I think you'd like it.'

She glanced at him sharply. 'Just how long have you been back in this area, Saul? Buying property, finding new restaurants? Why all this cloak-and-dagger secrecy?'

'Isn't that rather a case of the pot calling the kettle black?'

The derisive smile caught her on the raw. She looked quickly away again, and began sifting through the contents of the in-tray on her desk, trying very hard to ignore the drumming of her pulses. For some reason she was beginning to feel cornered, as if some master-plan was being cunningly executed. The illogical notion irritated her. What was it that Carol had said? She and Saul were behaving like paranoids with a persecution mania? Well, that could certainly be applied in her case at the moment.

'I'll call for you at eight,' Saul said quietly, putting his coffee-mug on a nearby shelf and eyeing the rows of rosettes with apparent approval. 'Make the effort and you might surprise yourself and actually enjoy it. Don't bother to show me around the stables, incidentally. Gina's very kindly given me a guided tour. You're a bit overcrowded, though quite a few are livery horses, I gather. But generally it's very impressive.' He turned at the door. 'Do you mind if I give that young

Cleveland Bay a workout in your paddock this morning?'

'Yes, I do. He's a potential showjumper, not a fancy polo pony. I'm schooling him myself.'

'Some other time, then.' Saul sounded infuriatingly unmoved.

She was too annoyed to speak as he sauntered away, furious with herself for her petty reaction. Why did Saul have to come back here, strolling around as if he owned the damned place? Why couldn't he just stay in Berkshire and amuse himself with his smart friends and his up-market sport and leave her in peace?

Her brooding resentment stubbornly refused to disperse. Even the tiniest female in the establishment proved far from immune to the legendary Gallagher charm, Francesca noted icily as Lowenna put Cobber, her little dapple-grey pony, through his paces in the indoor school later on, her wide grey eyes fixed unwaveringly on Saul for signs of approval.

'She's a bit "overhorsed", but for a child of. . .what is she? Three?' Saul glanced at her coolly. 'That's something that must be difficult to avoid.'

'It's better to learn on a pony that's too big than too small,' Francesca retorted through tight lips.

'Absolutely.' Saul's voice was dry.

'Isn't Cobber lovely?' Lowenna brought the pony over to them at a trot, and gazed from one to the other. 'Isn't he, Saul?'

'He's beautiful. And you ride very well.' The gleam of warmth in Saul's lidded gaze gave Francesca a pang somewhere in the region of her heart. When Lowenna insisted that Saul ride with her, she found her petty stricture about Vengeance being overruled, and watched Saul spring on to the big horse's back with such speed and lightness she blinked at the rush of memories it brought back. Saul rode with a style all his own. He looked as if he were part of a horse, weightless yet in complete control. How could she have conveniently forgotten that it was from Saul that she'd learned all anyone really needed to know about horses?

She suddenly felt small and mean and hopelessly tangled up inside. Why was she being so prickly? she asked herself miserably. No wonder Saul was looking so smugly amused the whole time. Wasn't her stiff defensiveness a pathetic give-away of her feelings? Wasn't she just showing him how much she'd missed him, how hurt she'd been when he went away that night and never came back?

Saul disappeared before lunch, saying he had some business to attend to, and calmly announcing that he'd booked a table at Raleighs and would be returning by a quarter to eight to take Francesca out for dinner. Since this was said in the very public and crowded location of the kitchen at lunchtime, in front of Carol, Ellen, Lowenna and an openly agog Mrs Prince, Francesca found herself in a painful dilemma. Her burning desire to tell Saul to go and jump in the River Exe was tempered by an awareness that she actually didn't have a good reason for refusing. Her touchy attitude around Saul could hardly have gone unnoticed. To turn down flat an offer of a meal out with the step-cousin she'd once idolised, and hadn't seen since her eighteenth birthday, would arouse suspicions she preferred to keep well and truly dormant.

So, mindful of this latest revelation, she accepted with as much good grace as she could muster, venting her suppressed anger in a gruelling few hours schooling Vengeance on the lunge-rope in the barn pasture.

At seven, when the last of the children's lessons were over, she dragged herself indoors and ran a hot bath, wrapping her hair in a towel to protect it from the steam, and, huddled in her cream bathrobe, she examined the contents of her wardrobe.

In the end, a three-piece in light mauve-blue crêpe de Chine with swirly ankle-length skirt and baggy jacket seemed to fit the occasion. In truth, it was months since she'd been out for a meal, she realised, sitting in front of the white-painted dressing-table in her bedroom and dragging the hairbrush ferociously through her long dark hair.

She eyed her reflection without enthusiasm. Too sallow, too thin, her face never pleased her much. The only redeeming features, if she forced herself to be totally objective about her looks, were her eyes. They were large, slightly slanting, deep-set above high cheekbones, their smoky hyacinth-blue accentuated by a fringe of thick black eyelashes which gave a dramatic effect even when she used no eyeshadow. Now, with some contrary urge to look her best tonight, she stroked a sliver of irridescent blue from a kohl pencil along upper and lower lids, and then leaned back to survey the effect. Not bad, she thought, slightly startled by the alteration in her appearance. Nerves were making her stomach clench into painful knots at the prospect of the evening ahead with Saul. Why was she doing this? Why couldn't she have been quietly assertive; calmly refused the invitation without incriminating herself by showing irritation or resentment?

Too late now. She'd made the commitment, and she'd just have to see it through. Painting her face and putting on her finery was unlikely to give Saul

Gallagher any false impressions. And at least it would bolster her sadly flagging confidence.

A light fluff of blusher on her cheekbones was added, some pinky brown lip-pencil on the smooth fullness of her lips, and a navy-blue clip to hold her heavy dark hair off her face.

As a final afterthought she sprayed herself with some of the French perfume Howard Graham had rashly given her after his last trip abroad before he'd headed off on his lecture trip around the UK. . .and she was ready.

After sliding her feet into low navy pumps and rummaging in the wardrobe for the matching clutch-bag, she darted along the corridor in time to read Lowenna a bedtime story.

'The one about the old man and the turnip and the mouse,' Lowenna announced, considerably testing Francesca's powers of recall as she searched through the bookcase. 'You smell nice.'

'Thank you, darling. So do you.' She gave the child a warm hug and inhaled the aroma of bubblebath and talcum powder with a smile.

'It's my Milly Mouse talcum powder. Ellen let me use it. She said it smells lovely.'

She cuddled the soft little body close, nuzzling her neck, 'It does. In fact you smell so lovely I could eat you all up——'

'Hello there. You two make a very attractive picture. Am I interrupting something?' Saul's voice came from the doorway, and they both looked round, Lowenna's laughing face lighting up even more. Francesca stared in silence, noting the expensive cut of his soft, brushed-cotton cream shirt and immaculate tan cords. A leather waistcoat gave his appearance just that hint of eccentricity, reminding her of the Saul she used to know.

Her throat constricted. Lord, he looked magnificient. With those long, muscular legs and wide supple shoulders, that brooding gypsy air of *containment*. . .

She found she was rigidly containing her own feelings deep inside her, as Saul was greeted with great approval and ordered to read to Lowenna instead. Of course, Saul's magical power over unruly horses and vicious dogs would naturally extend to impressionable and unusually precocious three-year-old girls, wouldn't it? Francesca tried hard to quell the growing knot of panic inside her, and ignored the enigmatic smile Saul angled at her as they finally left the sleepy child to snuggle down in bed, and made their way downstairs.

'You look nice,' he commented lightly as they emerged into the breezy spring evening and climbed into the Range Rover. 'You smell nice, too. Expensive perfume? The stables must be making a good profit.'

She reddened slightly, but refused to rise to the taunt. 'I'm glad you like the perfume. Actually, it was a present.' She wasn't sure why she said that, and immediately wished she hadn't as Saul's glance narrowed on her face.

'Ah. From an admirer?'

'From a friend.'

'A male friend.'

'Yes, a male friend. His name is Howard Graham. He has blond hair, blue eyes, he's a course constructor for the British Show Jumping Association and he's away on a lecture tour at the moment. Would you like any other information?'

'That will do for the moment.' Saul's tone was dangerously bland. She realised she'd touched him on the raw, and felt a disreputable stab of victory. It was quite ridiculous, of course. Her friendship with Howard Graham was a casual, on-off affair, partly because she was unwilling to commit herself to anything else, and partly because he was based up in Warwickshire and travelled around so much it would be very hard to make it more serious even if she wanted to.

Their drive into Exeter was accomplished in charged silence. But, by the time they had parked and walked into the Cathedral Square, Francesca's fleeting enjoyment of scoring petty points off Saul had vanished. She found that even the fierce anger she'd felt earlier in the day had dissipated. Suddenly she felt drained, and unutterably weary and sad. Yesterday her father had been buried. And tonight she was putting on an act, fencing, playing yet more games, going through the motions of being superficially polite and composed in Saul Gallagher's company, when what she really longed to do was run and hide.

'Don't look so tragic, Chessy.' Saul's voice was cool, but tinged with enough sympathy to bring a choked feeling to her throat.

'Don't. . . I'm all right.'

'Maybe this was insensitive of me, dragging you out with me tonight,' he mused quietly, his grey eyes assessing her tense pallor as they paused outside the restaurant, 'but it's been a long time, and I'm in no mood to prolong matters.'

'What is that supposed to mean?' Abruptly the alarm bells were ringing again, and she clenched her hands at her sides, her palms damp.

'Come on, let's go inside.' It was no answer, and the hooded gaze was unreadable as he held open the door for her and followed her into the dark, intimate interior of the restaurant.

Raleighs was a blend of old-English Elizabethan and Continental chic, with blackened beams and uneven floors offset by chintz-flowered oilcloth tablecloths and café curtains on brass poles across the windows. It was three-quarters full, a promising sign on a Thursday night. An impeccably polite head waiter ushered them into an alcove where a burgundy-coloured candle was flickering a halo of light. Someone had given their artistic talents full rein with a table decoration of pink rosebuds and gypsophila.

'Hungry?' Saul flicked her a half-smile as menus were conjured out of thin air and the wine-list was respectfully proffered. 'Their seafood was good when I came a few weeks ago. Do you still like scallops?'

'I suppose I do. . .'

'Try the scallop mousseline with caviare.'

'Saul, there are no prices on this menu.'

He ignored her muttered protest and leaned back in his chair to study the menu, his dark features expressionless. She stared woodenly at the ornate black script on vellum inside the heavy leather-bound folder, willing her stomach not to rumble. Her mouth was watering already, despite her wary reluctance to relax.

'They also do grilled scallops with a white wine and butter sauce, and *paupiettes* of sole with lobster stuffing. Do you want an aperitif, incidentally?'

'No, thanks.'

Saul glanced at the hovering waiter. 'Bring me a straight tonic with ice, no lemon, would you?'

'Right away, Mr Gallagher.'

She was feeling infuriatingly out of her depth all of a sudden. The sheltered nature of her life to date hadn't occurred to her until she stared at this opulent menu with its mind-boggling array of expensive food. Apart from the very rare outing with Howard Graham, who favoured pub snacks and would have a seizure if he saw the hedonistic contents of this menu, her social life revolved around fish fingers for Lowenna's tea and cheap and cheerful takeaways at Sarah's and Angus's village cottage.

'I'll have the tomato sorbet with prawns,' she announced at last with a valiant effort at decisiveness, flicking over to the main-course list, 'and then *mignons* of English lamb with basil, please.'

Saul chose the *paupiettes* of sole, and beef Wellington. The wine waiter was dispatched with orders for half-bottles of mineral water, Saint-Emilion Grand Cru, and a four-year-old Saumur to drink with the fish course. When they had been left in peace, Saul lifted his gaze to meet hers, his eyes penetrating.

'Will you just relax?' he suggested softly. 'Being with you feels like being permanently on red-alert.'

'Then you should have found someone else to take out for a meal.'

'Chessy, can we call a truce? Just for a couple of hours?' There was mockery in the deep voice but a gleam of sincerity somewhere in his eyes. She stared at him, every nerve in her body conscious of his closeness. How the hell did he expect her to relax, when he had this effect on her? she thought angrily. Why was he being so. . .*obtuse*? Surely, *surely* he hadn't forgotten what had happened the day after her party?

'Why have you come back, Saul?' She blurted it out, her voice shaky.

There was a pause. The grey eyes were intent on her

discomfort. 'Several reasons. One of them was to make sure you were all right——'

'Are you serious?'

'Absolutely.'

'After four years of silence, you suddenly decide to come and see if I'm all right?' She gave a short, disbelieving laugh. The waiter deposited their drinks on the table, and they went through the brief ceremony of wine tasting. She accepted a glass of the Saumur, and sipped it carefully.

'Until now you had your father.'

'You're not being very convincing,' she retorted acidly. 'My father only died this week, and you've obviously been planning to come back to Bellbridge for ages. You don't buy a house in seven days flat. Besides, you've been here, to this restaurant—a few weeks ago, you said. Why all the secrecy, for heaven's sake?'

Saul lifted a lean brown hand to push the black hair from his forehead, his eyes narrowing. 'I could ask you the same thing. On a scale of one to ten, my little deceptions score hardly at all compared with yours!'

'Oh, don't start that again——'

'I haven't even begun, Francesca.' His voice hardened. 'You know damn well there are at least half a dozen good reasons why I left you alone, stayed away from Bellbridge! You needed space to grow up, but you had your father jealously guarding your every move. You didn't seem to know what you wanted, but you certainly didn't need the extra complications *I* provided in your life.'

'How the hell do you know what I *needed*?'

He ignored her. 'My own life was confused at that time. I was living and travelling with the gypsies, getting to know my real father, trying to sort out my allegiances. . . That was a bad year for me; I was working hard at separating fantasy from reality. And that was something you had to do as well, and not with me around!'

She stared at him in the charged silence which followed, and the arrival of their first courses seemed a welcome diversion. The light dish of prawns and a piquant tomato sorbet was delicious. The flavour of the food seemed to mellow her tension a fraction. She wished she could relax, really enjoy this evening, instead of clinging to her defences and her anger and her growing suspicions that Saul was playing some kind of waiting game with her.

The lamb was exquisitely cooked and beautifully garnished, served with the freshest of peas, cauliflower and carrots arranged with creative ingenuity on a silver platter. While they ate Saul turned the conversation to less personal topics and she followed his lead, politely enquiring about the last polo season and relating Hill Mead's successes at the recent shows. They agreed the Saint-Emilion was extremely good, chose the same pudding course of coffee meringue gâteau, and had reached the coffee stage before Saul caught her eyes with a wry, enquiring smile.

'Feeling better now, Chessy?'

She stiffened automatically. 'That was a lovely meal. Thanks for bringing me. I fully intend paying my share, of course.'

'Don't be absurd. Our financial situations are not comparable.'

'I may not be saturated with wealth, as you now appear to be, Saul, but I'm not exactly penniless. And I don't want to feel. . .beholden to you—in any way.'

There was a long pause.

'Francesca. . . I'm sorry you feel so bitter. And I'm sorry if you felt. . .abandoned,' Saul said after a while, his tone thoughtful, 'but your father's attitude made it impossible for me to stick around. And it wasn't easy for my mother to keep in touch, either——'

'Will you stop talking as if I'm a helpless child who can't look after herself?' she demanded angrily. 'You talk of "abandoning" me, and of coming back to see if I'm all right! I wasn't a child when I last saw you, Saul, and I'm certainly able to look after myself and run my own life now.'

'Maybe.'

'What's *that* supposed to mean?'

'Maybe you can look after yourself now, but you were certainly a child four years ago, Francesca.' Saul levelled an intent, speculative gaze on her flushed face. 'You might have been celebrating your eighteenth birthday, but basically you were still a spoiled little daddy's girl. Used to getting what you wanted. . .'

She put her spoon down slowly, the colour receding from her cheeks as she saw the derisive challenge in his expression, and recalled in horror the past in all its intimate, embarrassing detail.

'. . .the fledgeling finally transforming into a swan, testing your powers on any hapless male in sight——'

'You haven't changed, have you?' she cut in icily. 'My father always called you "an arrogant gypsy bastard"—I'm beginning to see his point.'

She'd gone too far—she realised that instantly as she watched the swarthy face tighten into a hard mask.

'Inaccurate,' Saul retorted after a chilling silence, slivers of ice in his eyes. 'My birth may not have been covered by the legal Gorgio law of matrimony, although my mother and father married in a register office very soon afterwards. In any event, in the eyes of the Romanies I was born *in* wedlock, not outside it. Which is more than can be said for Lowenna!'

Francesca's fists clenched involuntarily in her lap. 'Keep Lowenna out of this!'

'Why? It seems to me that Lowenna is. . .pivotal to the whole sorry tale.'

'Well, perception never was your strong point. People with the sensitivity of a rhinoceros sadly *lack* perception!'

'Is that really how you see me now?' Saul sounded thoughtful. 'I'll tell you how *I* see things, shall I? Your version of reality was always spiced up with your romantic gypsy fantasies. Not many men could measure up to those, could they? Although there was quite a fan club trying!'

She shivered, suddenly frightened of the dark depths of bitterness which seemed to have been dredged up between them.

'Not even a true-life experience with the genuine article could satisfy you, could it?' he persisted bitingly. 'No sooner had you tasted your forbidden fruit, sampled your much-longed-for "bit of rough", than you trotted straight back into the arms of one of the "suitable suitors" Daddy had bestowed his blessing on!'

'Saul, please. . .' There was a bleakness in his eyes. The mockery had gone. Somewhere, deep within her confused reaction to his lethal attack, she felt surprise at the extent of his bitterness.

'He wasn't quite so suitable, after all, though, was he, the well-connected, "suitable" Mr Julian Harrington-Green?'

The softly sardonic voice made her flinch. Saul was

twisting the proverbial knife with a sadistic lack of squeamishness.

'Since presumably he ran a mile when he discovered the price he had to pay for receiving the warm glow of paternal approval? Or maybe it wasn't him at all? I'm intrigued, Francesca. Tell me, which one of those chinless wonders dancing attendance at your eighteenth birthday party was it? Which one managed to father your child? Julian Harrington-Green? Neville Beresford? Anton Lennox?'

'Go to *hell*, Saul. . .' Close to tears of fury and humiliation, she sprang to her feet so jerkily that she tipped over a coffee-cup and the remains of her glass of wine, and, uncaring of the speculative glances from the rest of the diners, she turned blindly and dashed from the restaurant into the damp spring evening outside.

CHAPTER FOUR

A STEADY drizzle had taken the place of the earlier dry weather, and as Francesca emerged the heavens seemed to open, the rain quickly penetrating the fine wool of the navy Paisley shawl she'd slung over her suit. Unsure at first where she was heading, she clutched the shawl round her, put her head down and ran towards South Street, wishing she could remember exactly where the nearest telephone box was. How could you live in an area all your life and not know where the telephone boxes were? she wondered distractedly, aware that there were tears running down her face, causing curious glances from passers-by.

At least years of being a dutiful Brownie and Girl Guide had drilled into her the wisdom of carrying coins for the payphone at all times, she thought with bitter humour, along with safety-pins, Elastoplast and a spare handkerchief.

She'd spotted the kiosk, and was fumbling blindly in her clutch-bag for money just as Saul's harsh shout made her spin round and drop the bag and its contents into the nearest puddle.

'Francesca, in hell's name. . .' He sprinted up, his expression thunderous, barely out of breath although if he'd stayed to settle the bill and run all the way after her he must have been going at a daunting speed. 'What the devil do you think you're doing?'

'Ringing for a taxi. Excuse me.'

She'd bent and fished the bag out of the water,

located the coin, and pushed her way past him and into the phone booth before he grabbed hold of her with both hands, forcibly restraining her.

'If you want to go home, I'll drive you. Stop being bloody hysterical——'

'Take your hands off me!'

'Not until you calm down and act your age!'

'Let *go* of me! I loathe you, Saul; I never want to see you again. . .' Sobs were rending her now, and blindly she kicked at his shins, uncaring of their surroundings, wrestling with his chillingly superior strength until she felt as if she'd burst with frustration. Saul jerked her so hard against him that the breath was catapulted from her body in a shocked gasp, and she felt herself crushed to his powerful length, conscious of his muscled body in every tiny nerve and cell, the insidious transformation from violent resistance to sexual awareness fuelling her efforts to get away.

'Chessy, stop fighting me. We're causing a traffic jam as it is.' The rueful words were bitten out through clenched teeth, as her fierce kicks and punches continued unabated.

'Need any help, miss?' The enquiry came from a uniformed police constable in the company of a smart WPC, who were standing assessing the scene with the ominously polite but watchful expression of the professional peace-keeper.

Saul released her, and Francesca swayed involuntarily, the furious tussle, combined with the wine she'd drunk and her headlong flight here, leaving her feeling almost faint.

'Yes,' she heard herself saying in a cold, shaky voice which sounded like someone else's. 'This man was assaulting me.'

'Chessy, for heaven's sake, don't be such a bloody idiot.' Saul's low voice was incredulous, taut with fury.

'Do you know this man, madam?' The constable and the policewoman were exchanging glances.

'She's known me all her blasted life,' Saul supplied shortly, fury driving all the colour from his swarthy face, making his eyes look as black as coal in the lurid streetlamp overhead.

He was staring at Francesca as he spoke, and she numbly stared back at him, her heart drumming. The rain was getting heavier. She must look like a drowned rat, she reflected inconsequentially. Raindrops were dripping from her soaked hair down her face, mingling with the tears. Her thin silky evening suit was clinging damply to the shape of her body in what she knew must be a lamentably revealing fashion. The full skirt was wet against her thighs.

Her breathing still jerky and laboured, she gazed at Saul in silence. The rain had plastered his dark hair to his head, and the cream shirt was beginning to mould itself to his chest under the leather waistcoat, faithfully outlining the rigid contours of muscles chiselled to perfection via the rigours of the polo field. The police constable was tall, but Saul topped him by at least two inches.

'Is that true?' the officer was asking, with a keen inspection of her tear-stained face and trembling limbs. 'Is this man a friend of yours?'

'I know him, but he's not a friend. I want to go home, but he's followed me here.'

'I'm her step-cousin,' Saul ground out, his voice dangerously soft, 'so let's just stop this farce and I'll drive her home.'

'Being related to the young lady doesn't give you the

right to manhandle her, sir,' the policeman cut in briskly. 'I think you'd better give me your name and address.' A notebook was produced, and the crackle of a radio could be heard relaying indecipherable messages.

Francesca found she could no longer support herself on her own legs. She leaned weakly back against the phone box, suddenly so drained that the scene unfolding itself in front of her seemed like a distant happening, unrelated to her. Her legs felt like rubber, her hands were shaking, and her teeth were chattering with nerves and cold.

Saul was curtly supplying his name, giving Leigh Barton as his address, and Francesca shook her head silently when asked if she wanted to bring any charges against him. She wished she could just stop shaking and crying. She wished she could answer the questions the police officers were gently but persistently asking her in a coherent manner.

Finally, at the suggestion of the WPC a police-car was radioed from its tour of the city streets near by to drive her home. She was helped into the back by the policewoman and driven away, leaving Saul standing there on the pavement with the young male constable, the whole outlandish scene reminiscent of one of those melodramatic old black and white detective films shown on television on Sunday afternoons.

'Oh, hell, I'm sorry to be such a nuisance,' she managed to say as they finally halted outside Hill Mead. 'I feel such a fool. We'd been out for a meal, and then he—I mean I. . .'

'Don't worry, love,' the policewoman's grin was encouraging but worldly-wise as Francesca climbed out, 'we meet all sorts in this job. People with personal problems go in for all sorts of funny behaviour, believe me. Go out for a meal with someone else in future, if your step-cousin has that effect on you. Goodnight.'

Having taken a hot shower, she expected another sleepless night. But after a brief conjecture on how long it would have taken Saul to extricate himself from the zealous attention of the police officer, get back to the car park and retrieve his car, and an even briefer and less enjoyable speculation on Saul's mood the next time she'd meet him, she fell into a deep, utterly dreamless sleep, unbroken until morning, waking reluctantly to hear Carol's voice gently saying her name.

She opened her eyes, for a few seconds totally unable to recall where she was, then sat up with a jolt.

'My turn to bring you tea and toast in bed this morning.' The older woman smiled, depositing a tray adorned with a crisp white cloth, matching folded napkin, and even a tiny cut-glass vase containing a single yellow crocus. The morning's post was tucked between the plate and the cup.

'The crocus was Lowenna's idea. She helped me lay your tray.'

'Carol, this is so sweet of you, but you really shouldn't have bothered——' Francesca stopped short, spotting the time and giving a yelp of dismay. 'Oh, crikey, look at the time! I must get up.' Catching a glimpse of herself in the dressing-table mirror, she winced at the sight she presented, her hair sticking out in all directions and hanging in a wild, tangled bush down her back, dark smudges round her eyes, chalk-white cheeks. . . Compared with Carol's captivating appearance, in a yellow flower-patterned skirt and matching blouse, she felt a freak.

'Stay where you are,' Carol said soothingly. 'It's only a quarter past nine. I've checked with Gina and she can cope quite easily for the next hour or so——'

'But it's Caxford Hall Show tomorrow! We'll be frantically busy getting everything ready. . .'

'Gina can cope,' Carol repeated calmly. 'Just sit there in bed and enjoy your breakfast and relax for half an hour, Chessy, darling. You're trying to do too much.'

'Rubbish. I live a life of pampered luxury and you know it!' Francesca subsided for a moment, taking a sip of tea and letting its reviving warmth spread through her with deep gratitude. 'If you think I have a hard time looking after the stables and Lowenna at the same time, remember I have loads of help.'

'Help costs money, though,' Carol pointed out reflectively, taking the second cup of tea off the tray for herself and perching on Francesca's blue duvet. 'Are you sure you're not going to be overstretched, now your father's died? Will there be any inheritance tax to pay, for instance?'

'I'm not sure. You know what Dad was like—he wasn't the great communicator! But he made the stables over to me by Deed of Gift a few years back. There may be some tax, but nothing too crippling. I'm seeing the solicitors on Tuesday; I'll know more then. The main problem is lack of profitability—two and a half per cent on turnover isn't exactly riches, you'll agree. That's really why I want this extra land. . .' Francesca yawned suddenly, and took a bite of toast and honey. 'But you don't want to be bored with all that. . .'

'Is your breakfast to your liking, by the way?' Carol

asked suddenly. 'Lowenna's a mine of information. She said you like milky tea and honey on your toast.

'Absolutely correct. Where is she. She's normally hurled herself into my bed long before now.'

'Helping Mrs Prince to fold up the washing. I thought you might appreciate a lie-in, *and* a short spell of peace and quiet this morning.'

Francesca grinned. 'I get the feeling I'm going to miss you when you go back!'

'Oh, I meant to tell you. Saul rang this morning.'

Francesca felt herself go very still.

'He spent his first night at Leigh Barton last night. He's asked if I'd like to stay on a few days, re-acquaint myself with the old place.' Carol's blue eyes twinkled. 'And, as the university can spare me for a week and I haven't seen more than fleeting glimpses of my one and only son for the last four years, and as I'd also very much like to get better acquainted with my little great-niece, I've jumped at the offer.'

'That's lovely.' She couldn't quite keep the shake out of her voice.

Carol glanced at her curiously. 'I promise faithfully not to get underfoot,' she added lightly.

'You couldn't get underfoot if you tried. Sorry, I didn't mean to sound offhand.'

'How did your evening out go?' Carol's voice was carefully neutral.

'Fine. We had a good meal at Raleighs in Exeter.' Francesca pushed the tray along her knees a little way and began to open the letters, carefully avoiding Saul's mother's eyes, slitting open a letter from the agricultural department of the estate agents confirming that her offer for the twenty acre field had been received. She made a mental note to seek final clearance from the bank and follow it up next week. That extra land would make quite a difference to the astronomic bills for hay she was having at the moment. . .

'Saul said you came home quite early.'

'Did he?' Francesca's eyes were suddenly bleak as she pushed back the duvet and abruptly jumped out of bed. 'Carol, thanks for breakfast. And I'm delighted your're going to be staying near by for a while. But I have to get down to the stables and do some work.'

'I'll leave you to it, then.' Carol collected the tray, hesitating at the door. 'Chessy, love, if you want to talk. . .have a "heart to heart" about anything, you do know you can trust me, don't you?'

'Of course. Stop fretting about me. I'm fine!' Her answering smile was over-bright, and, turning away, she absorbed herself with trying to brush the tangles from her hair until she heard Carol quietly go out and close the door behind her.

An outward brittle calm seemed to persist over the next twenty-four hours, throughout the chaotic preparations for the show and the hundred-and-one other matters which jostled for attention. But, inwardly, Francesca felt strung up to screaming pitch. Stress seemed to make everything more of a struggle. Selecting the horses, grooming them *and* the various students who were competing on them to a peak of perfection worthy of Hill Mead's reputation suddenly seemed the most daunting task she'd tried to supervise; even organising the simple but vital accessories, the tack, the head-collars, the water-buckets, liaising with pupils and their fond parents anxious that their offspring bring home a rosette—every aspect of the event taxed her stamina and resilience to the maximum.

It was the ominous silence from Saul making her feel like this, she reflected as she and Gina drove the Hill Mead horsebox and motorised caravan in stately convoy up the M5 at the crack of dawn on Saturday morning. She wasn't normally jittery and on edge, although what she imagined he was about to do in retaliation she had no idea. Retaliation was childish, and Saul was certainly not that. In fact, he'd always possessed a maturity beyond his years. But conversely his pride and his unpredictable temper were legendary.

Resolutely she put him out of her mind as they joined the growing queue of cars and horseboxes leading into the glorious Caxford Hall estate, finding pleasure as always in the magnificent sweep of the grounds surrounding the eighteenth century splendour of the Devon-pink Caxford Hall. As this show was on a Saturday, Lowenna and Ellen were with her, and she listened to her daughter's disjointed chatter as she commented on everything she saw. Lowenna adored horse shows, and loved to come and watch whenever she was allowed to.

'I'll ride Cobber at the show, Mummy, won't I?' Lowenna appeared behind the driving-seat as they finally drew up by the collecting ring and prepared to unfasten the ramps. 'Ellen says I won't!'

'Ellen's right, sweetheart. You're not quite old enough to ride Cobber at horse shows, Wenna.' Francesca bent down and gave the small child a fierce hug and kissed her turned-up nose, laughing at the stubborn pout. 'You can watch and see if Mummy's stables win any rosettes!'

Vengeance was being led down the ramp by Lydia, one of the Assistant Instructor students from the agricultural college, who was neatly turned out in freshly washed breeches and black riding jacket. With his mane tightly plaited, sweating slightly beneath his navy and gold Hill Mead rug, Vengeance looked wonderful. The powerful muscles rippled beneath the conker-coloured coat, glistening impressively in the surprisingly warm sunshine, and Francesca felt a faint twinge of excitement in spite of her edgy mood.

She was going to enter him for the open jumping and ride him herself. For the purpose she'd dug out her best tight white breeches and navy-blue riding coat, coiled her freshly washed and plaited hair into a glossy dark bun at her nape, and polished her black riding boots until they shone like jet. It was ages since she'd personally entered a class on any of her horses. With the pressures of her father's illness and the demands of caring for a small baby, she'd been content to take a back seat and let Gina and various students and pupils compete instead. Now, though, and just for the sheer hell of it, the challenge of entering Vengeance for his very first competition was what she needed to boost her shaky morale.

'Could you saddle up Vengeance for me, please, Lyddy? I'll put him over some practice jumps in a while. Gina, could you keep an eye out for the junior jumps going up, and watch out for our pupils when they arrive? Wenna and I are off to find an ice-cream, aren't we, poppet?'

'Ice-cream?' Lowenna's dark head nodded emphatically, and, hand in hand, they set off across the already pitted ground, threading their way through the growing crowds of families, camera-slung fathers and mothers with pushchairs, dodging the occasional mounted and numbered competitor riding through the throng.

'Would you like a choc-ice or a cornet with a chocolate flake?'

'Well, well, fancy seeing you here.' The deep, sardonic voice shattered Francesca's composure. She stopped in her tracks, her eyes swivelling in dismay towards Saul's tall figure blocking their path, resplendent in brown leather boots, white jodhpurs and soft tweed jacket, and then moving to the willowy ash-blonde woman at his side, sunglasses pushed stylishly to the top of her head, whose cool brown eyes were regarding her with undisguised interest. A rapid mental computation identified her instantly as the car-phone-using Daihatsu driver. Francesca's heart did another painful lurch.

'Saul!' Lowenna easily made up for her own marked lack of enthusiasm. 'Mummy's buying me an ice-cream. Do you want one too?'

Saul squatted down on his haunches and treated Lowenna to one of his heart-stopping smiles. 'I've just had one. Maybe I'll buy you another one later?'

'Yes, please!'

'What a sweet little thing,' the ash-blonde was murmuring in a low, cultured, husky voice guaranteed to draw any male within a two-mile radius. 'How old is she?'

'Three.' Francesca forced herself to speak civilly, a monumental effort which seemed to involve her teeth in a great deal of rigid clenching.

'So forward! My brother has a three-year-old who can barely string two words together!' the girl drawled, tossing back her feathery shoulder-length hair and arching her eyebrows at Saul. 'Aren't you going to introduce us, darling?'

Saul straightened easily, inclining his head with a

curt nod. His daunting air of self-containment had never been more noticeable.

'Francesca—this is Charmian Baron. Charmian—Francesca St Aubyn and her daughter Lowenna.'

The graciously extended hand was silky smooth, as elegant as the fine cream wool culottes and tailored jacket which draped with mannequin perfection over the reed-thin figure, and Francesca inspected her more closely. Heart-shaped gold earrings dangled discreetly from the woman's ears. She had a straight nose, good cheekbones, and perfectly even white teeth. The name Baron rang a distant bell, but, with the usual pang of guilt on Lowenna's behalf, Francesca watched Charmian's eyes flick deliberately towards her ringless fingers, and the vague jolt of memory faded.

It didn't get any easier, just because *she* was acclimatised to her socially irregular situation. But there hadn't been much she could have done about it. In the absence of Lowenna's real father, she hadn't been prepared to compromise with a substitute. And in a tiny village like Bellbridge it would have been quite pointless trying to play the hypocrite, buy herself a ring and call herself by a fictional married name! But ultimately it was Lowenna who suffered, she knew, and the knowledge made her feel helpless and angry.

The pain of those past decisions flitted like a rapid fast-forward through her mind as she watched Charmian Baron's silent judgement, just as she'd watched so many others. Maybe she was getting over-sensitive, she chided herself quickly. Maybe she was developing a chip on her shoulder, in which case she should make stern efforts to shake it off. People with chips on their shoulders were among the least attractive people she knew.

'Lowenna *is* very advanced for her age. She's amazing her playgroup leader by writing her name and reading everything she can lay her hands on. Apparently they're not supposed to do that until they're four. What are you doing here, anyway?' she heard herself asking Saul with commendable sang-froid, as Lowenna began to get restive and tugged her mother towards the ice-cream van where a queue was already beginning to form despite the early hour. 'Have you decided to ditch polo completely and take up show-jumping?'

The hard mouth twitched into a smile which made no pretence of warmth. The look in his eyes made it clear that the outlandish culmination of their meal out together was far from forgiven or forgotten. She felt her stomach tighten in a wave of apprehension, then anger that he could make her feel guilty and defensive just by the expression in his eyes.

'No. I've been invited along by the organisers to present the prizes.'

'Oh—the local celebrity guest? How exciting.'

'Mummy, my ice-cream! You said you'd buy me an ice-cream!'

'So I did. Excuse us, would you?' She flashed a quick, impersonal smile at Saul and his friend, and turned away to join the queue, aware out of the corner of her eye as she did so that another man had greeted Saul and the *soignée* Charmian before they could move away—clearly a fellow polo player, since the talk was of January's high-goal matches out in Florida and the home fixtures within the next few weeks. Saul's responses were ambiguous. By the time the ice-cream was bought and she and Lowenna had made their surreptitious escape through the crowds, she'd overheard enough to feel a sharp stab of curiosity about

Saul's plans for the future. What was he up to? she mused, wending her way back to the horse lines and leaving Lowenna in the safe charge of Ellen, while she switched into top organising gear to run her little outfit as efficiently as possible.

Surely he wasn't *really* planning to opt out of professional polo and bury himself in the depths of the Devon countryside at Leigh Barton? He'd hinted that he was transferring his yard down here, but that overheard conversation just now hadn't given the impression he was particularly committed to the coming short English season, let alone the travelling involved in professional polo playing as the year progressed. . .

The day wore on, with the early sun disappearing and a chill wind blowing up from the west again. Classes were entered, Hill Mead began to add to their collection of rosettes with two wins in the junior jumping and a couple more in the gymkhana events, and, by the time the open jumping had dragged on for an hour longer than scheduled, Francesca was beginning to feel the strain on her nerves and her muscles. Vengeance was performing miracles, catapulting over the jumps as if he were an experienced show-jumper instead of a carefully brought on novice enjoying his first taste of competition. They had a few faults each time, but a lot of other competitors notched up faults too.

After endless jump-offs, and nerve-racking waits while the course was constantly rebuilt, she was astonished to find herself picking up third prize. The ordeal of receiving her rosette and prize from Saul, a cool, taciturn figure ensconced behind the green baize table with the judges, was overshadowed both by pleasure in

Vengeance's achievement and by the worsening weather conditions, with the rising wind now gusting around the showground, flapping the canvas of the judges' tent and sending people scurrying for previously discarded jackets and headscarves.

'Did you see Vengeance getting his rosette, sweetheart?' She laughed, jumping down as Lowenna ran to meet her. 'Wasn't he clever?'

'Cleverer than Cobber,' Lowenna agreed wistfully, reaching up a small hand to pat the powerful flank. 'Can I ride him?'

'No, darling, Vengeance is much too big for you to ride. I promise you can enter Cobber for competitions as soon as you're old enough. Maybe you could have a ride on Daffodil in a minute, when Susie brings him back from the gymkhana events.'

'I *like* Vengeance,' Lowenna insisted crossly, her dark little face crumpling into illogical tears, showing signs of a long, tiring day. Francesca exchanged rueful glances with Ellen, who was hovering near by, dividing her attention between watching the happenings in the show ring and keeping tabs on her small charge.

'Go into the caravan with her, could you, Ellen?' she asked quietly. 'We'll wind up here as soon as we can.'

Distracting her attention was Gina, gesticulating wildly at the side of the collecting ring, apparently involved in an argument with one of the pupils' pushier mothers. Leaving Lyddy to put the sweat-rug on Vengeance, Francesca was just wending her way through the milling crowds to referee when a flat, harsh voice stopped her in her tracks.

'You did well—congratulations.' She turned warily to see Saul, hands thrust in the pockets of his jodhpurs, surveying her through narrowed eyes. Her stomach tightened apprehensively. He was on his own now. Where was the fair Charmian? she wondered fleetingly. The blonde's eyes had held such a possessive gleam, she'd somehow expected her to be stuck on like cement.

'Thanks.'

'He's a promising young horse. Have you been schooling him yourself?'

'Yes.'

'And do you make a habit of dragging Lowenna around the horse shows while you amuse yourself competing?'

Her throat dried. The gloves were off, then. She felt isolated in the thronging crowds around them, conscious only of Saul's grey eyes boring relentlessly into her.

'Stay out of my affairs, Saul.'

'You don't seem in any hurry to find out if I spent the other night behind bars.'

He was gazing with cool arrogance at the length of her slender thighs in the tight white breeches, his eyes moving upwards to her face again with a flicker of what she thought was contempt in his eyes.

In spite of herself, her cheeks flushed slightly as the ludicrous finale to their evening out came flooding back to her.

'I gather you managed to retain your freedom?'

'Just about. I was let off with a caution. I'm probably on police files now as a potential molester of young women on the city streets.'

'Probably.' She resisted the urge to apologise. 'Look, excuse me, there are things I have to do.'

The heated conversation in the distance was looking set to get out of hand; Gina was a good stable manager but lacked a little in the diplomacy stakes. Francesca began to push past Saul.

'Just a minute. . .' His grip was firm on her upper arm. 'Where the hell do you think you're going?'

'Where I'm going is none of your business,' she hissed furiously, his touch obliterating all worthy attempts at cool civility as she tried to shake loose without attracting attention from the people near them. 'But, if you must know, I have to go and talk to one of my pupils' mothers——'

'You'd be better off examining your own role as a mother, Francesca,' he drawled acidly, 'because, however good a rider she is for her age, unless I'm very wrong I doubt if a three-year-old child should be climbing. . .' he gave an abrupt nod in the direction of the Hill Mead horseboxes '. . .unsupervised, on to the back of a young seventeen-hand horse with a decidedly unpredictable nature.'

CHAPTER FIVE

FRANCESCA turned, and went cold inside for a few seconds, glimpsing the scene by the horse lines. Lydia appeared to have tethered Vengeance to the line, leaving him sweating and trembling after his immense effort in the show ring, and had struck up an intimate conversation with Ellen, both of them apparently blissfully unaware of the small, determined child scaling Vengeance's stirrup leather and hauling herself upwards by the girth, while the horse stirred and side-stepped restlessly.

'Oh, no, Wenna!'

Saul restrained her headlong dash, his fingers clamping her arm with negligent strength.

'Wait; think,' he advised curtly. 'You'll scare them both if you go charging over there in hysterics——'

'I'm not a total fool,' she snapped, wrenching herself out of his grip and marching over to do battle. Within a matter of seconds the little drama was over. Lowenna was plucked to safety and Francesca had vented her pent-up fury on a scarlet-faced Ellen and Lydia, before taking Lowenna over to the caravan and tucking her up in one of the bunks for a much-needed afternoon nap. Emerging, still shaking inwardly, she found Saul propped against the rear of the horsebox, his expression deadpan.

'No damage done,' she said tautly, aware that her knees were still shaking.

'She could have been badly injured.'

'I do realise that. But Vengeance isn't a monster.'

'Watching his antics in the show ring, he's hardly got the riding-hack temperament for a three-year-old.' Saul's voice was a flat, cool drawl, betraying no inkling of his feelings.

'Of course he hasn't.'

'How did he come by his name?'

'He was so badly behaved when Dad bought him it was a unanimous decision. It was bad management; boredom. I've cured him of all that—he's a reformed character these days.' She wished he'd just go away, stop leaning there so nonchalantly, judging her, criticising her with his eyes. . . 'Look, that was a near miss, but it turned out to be a storm in a teacup. It won't happen again.'

'How can you be so sure, when your young nanny seems to spend half her life daydreaming?'

Guilt was making her feel angrily defensive. Saul's whole unspoken message seemed to be implying that she was irresponsible, unfit to be the mother of a three-year-old child, selfish to be trying to juggle motherhood and a career. She restrained the urge to scream, taking a long, steadying breath and keeping her temper quietly under control.

'Ellen is kind, and patient with Lowenna. Frankly, she's the best nanny I've had in a long time.'

'You've had several?'

'Not that it's any of your business, Saul,' she managed with commendable politeness, 'but, yes. Good nannies don't grow on trees. And they tend to be very expensive.'

'Are you short of money?'

'No. . .but I'm not made of it, either!'

There was a long pause, as if he was assessing that

outburst with analytic thoroughness. 'So what are your plans for the stables? Judging by today's performance, you're seriously committed now to your career with horses. You could take your show-jumping a lot further. Is that your intention?'

She shook her head slowly, watching Lyddy out of the corner of her eye as she meticulously placed Vengeance's sweat-rug over his glistening back and prepared to load him into the lorry.

'No. I'm happy building up the teaching and livery side.' Serious competition in the show-jumping circuits would take her away from Lowenna too much, but she refrained from saying that to Saul. He would think she was trying to justify herself, and why the hell should she justifiy herself in his eyes? There was nothing to justify, for heaven's sake!

'I'm buying some land along my eastern boundary.'

Saul raised an eyebrow. 'Where your land adjoins mine?'

She flinched slightly. It *was* Saul's now. Of course. All that farmland abutting Hill Mead, and stretching a good few miles north and south of Hill Mead as well. . .

'More or less. There's a twenty-acre strip running between the Leigh Barton birch wood and the barn pasture where your land curves in close to my stables. Coombe Farm is selling it off. I've had my eye on it for a while now.'

'Is it up for auction?' Impossible to detect the underlying reason behind Saul's questions. Flushing slightly, she shook her head again.

'Offers around a guideline price.'

'And you know roughly how much to offer?'

'Oh, lord, you really do think I'm wet behind the

ears, don't you?' she shot at him witheringly. 'Yes, I think I'm just intelligent enough to take professional advice and work that out for myself, thanks, Saul.'

'And you've no problems financing the purchase?' A slight frown creased the dark line of his eyebrows now.

'I'll manage,' she explained with a deliberate touch of sarcasm. 'It's a question of balancing things. Profits are down because of the high price of feed and the overheads involved with keeping so many horses stabled. Initially the outlay on the extra land will make a hole in the balance sheets, but in the long run it will improve the overall profitability of the business. Am I going over your head?'

There was a short silence, during which the gleam of amusement in Saul's eyes became a glint of laughter.

'No, I think I'm just intelligent enough to grasp your point, thanks, Chessy,' he mimicked softly.

Her frosty composure was badly rocked as he levered himself off his leaning-post and sauntered towards her, gazing down at her with an unfathomable expression.

'Maybe I over-reacted just now,' he murmured calmly, disarming her a fraction. 'I once saw a small child crushed by a stampeding horse, out in South America. It made something of an imprint in my mind. Perhaps I've become over-cautious where children are concerned.'

Somehow his nearness, and the sincerity in his voice, had made her throat constrict. 'That's awful. . .' The mental image of his words made her feel slightly sick. If anything ever happened to Lowenna, life wouldn't be worth living. For want of something to say to break the charged silence, she said, 'What about *your* plans? Your polo plans, I mean?'

'In what respect?'

'I mean, usually you'd be out in Argentina at the moment, wouldn't you? Having "wintered" in Florida since January?' She mocked the glamorous lifestyle with her tone. 'Surely you're not serious about spending most of your time in this country?'

'If you've really been following my movements these last four years, you should know I'm usually in England in May.' He tilted a derisive eyebrow at her.

'I haven't been following your movements at all! But everyone knows what you polo professionals get up to all year long.'

'Do they indeed?'

She stared at him in annoyance. Did he have to make her feel as if he was constantly amusing himself with her? She was just realising how little she knew about Saul's life over the last four years. All she really knew was he'd taken a major gamble with the money left to him from Uncle Harry, a keen polo player and influential member of the Hurlingham Polo Association, and gone abroad to further a polo career begun initially during Pony Club and then in his years at Oxford.

The rest of her knowledge was sketchily gleaned from reports in *Horse and Hound* and *The Field*, and occasional articles in the Sunday glossies. According to these, Saul and other professionals like him, most of whom appeared to be South American, spent their lives travelling from one country to another, from Florida to Argentina, to England and then to France, and back to Argentina again at the end of the year. It was an annual schedule during which they were paid astronomic salaries for boosting the handicap score of various patrons blessed with the money to—rather unfairly—buy themselves a winning team.

But rumour had it that Saul had also made himself a fortune from horse-dealing. That was an area where, she imagined, his unerring Romany eye for horses must give him a distinct advantage.

'My plans are very flexible,' Saul said, watching her face closely, his own expression bland.

'Are you planning on playing in all the high-goal matches this season?'

'Possibly. I injured my shoulder a couple of months ago. A lot depends on how that shapes up. Plus other factors.'

'You're not being exactly forthcoming!' She'd blurted it out in frustration before she'd thought about it, furious at the gleam in his eyes.

'I'm flattered you're so interested in my future, Chessy.'

'I'm interested in your plans for Leigh Barton. Since it adjoins my property, I'd like to be kept informed of any major alterations in the pipeline,' she said stiffly, avoiding that mocking gaze.

'I do have plans. . . They're in the embryo stage at present. I'd like to open a polo training school,' Saul murmured laconically, adding by way of an after-thought, 'Incidentally, could I ask a favour? I'd like to stable a couple of my horses at Hill Mead initially. The stable-block at Leigh Barton needs a lot of attention. I'd pay full livery fees, of course.'

'I suppose so.' She was aware of sounding appallingly ungracious. She couldn't help it. 'Your mother told me you'd moved in now. How are you settling in?'

'Come and see. I'm having a housewarming party next Friday.'

She stiffened involuntarily. Saul watched her reaction with a narrowed gleam in his eyes.

'What's the matter? Worried about stepping inside the wolf's lair? Don't forget—my mother's going to be there for the next week or so.'

'I'm not worried about any such thing.'

'Good. Then to prove there are no ill feelings after Thursday night's little charade, come over for Sunday lunch tomorrow as well.'

She blinked at him angrily. The full onslaught of Saul's subtle, continuous pressure, a pressure he'd been exerting ever since he'd reappeared at the funeral, suddenly hit her.

'I'll think about it. My diary gets pretty full. I normally see Sarah and Angus on Sundays.'

'Look. . .' it was as if he were touching her with his eyes, and she shivered involuntarily '. . .what happened on Thursday night was not my idea of a joke. I exercised a considerable amount of control in not coming up to Hill Mead and giving you a bloody good hiding on Friday morning.'

This was drawled; deadpan. It was impossible to tell if he was serious or not.

'Don't make bully-boy threats to me! After all, there's my friend at the police station! All I have to do is ring her!' Her smile was saccharine sweet, but just a touch shaky under the unnerving laser-ray of Saul's scrutiny.

'That's probably a good thing. Harbouring violent feelings isn't a healthy state of mind.'

'No, it isn't. It beats me why you keep seeking me out like this, since you obviously hate the sight of me!'

'Hate the sight of you?' The hard grey gaze was suddenly bleaker. 'No, Chessy, way off mark as usual. I thought you'd matured. But everything is still black and white with you, isn't it?'

'Why can't you just leave me alone, Saul?' The shake in her voice was betraying her. Anger and bitterness and confusion suddenly felt a volatile mixture to control. Gina was coming their way, having finished her argument by the ring, but she hesitated a few yards away, glancing curiously from one to the other, then veered off in another direction with uncharacteristic tact.

'Chessy, I said some things on Thursday night in the heat of the moment.' His face had tightened a fraction. 'I'm not too proud to apologise.'

'I——'

'Come over tomorrow. You can look over the old house again.' The deep voice was low, difficult to gauge. Not pleading exactly—she couldn't imagine Saul ever pleading for anything, not even for his life; that macho arrogance went too deep: there was layer on layer of it, right through to the core—but there was a ring of genuine warmth which brought the old, long-ago days of the past creeping back, and tugged at her heart-strings and made the panic stir in her stomach. He must know how much she longed to visit Leigh Barton again——

'No, I can't. Not tomorrow.' No chance, she thought shakily. The mere thought of being closeted with Saul, in the intimate, nostalgia-evoking atmosphere of that house, was too much to contemplate.

'Then come to the housewarming.'

'I'll see——'

'There you are, Saul!' Charmian Baron had appeared, her blonde hair plastered across her face in the strong breeze, looking fractionally less *soignée* and far from pleased, with a dark-haired man in tow. 'We're supposed to be going up to the Hall for drinks with the rest of the VIPs, darling. Gabriel and I have been looking everywhere for you!'

The man beside her grinned cheerfully at Saul, raising an interested eyebrow at Francesca as she stood in silence. A cold knot was forming in her stomach as she noticed Charmian's possessive attitude towards Saul, and, try as she might, she couldn't seem to dislodge it. She took her mind off her growing misery by concentrating her attention on Gabriel. He was shorter than Saul, thicker-set and, if anything, darker, his skin and hair and eyes betraying foreign origins.

'Hello there!' he purred at her, laughing at Saul. 'I can see Saul has forgotten his manners. I am Gabriel Andrada.' The handshake was firm and warm. The deep voice held a strong trace of Spanish accent.

'Francesca St Aubyn. How do you do?'

'A great deal better for meeting you!'

'Gabriel is an old friend from South America. He has an unfortunate habit of trying his Latin charm on every female he meets.' There was an unmistakable sliver of ice in Saul's voice, quickly noted by Charmian who caught hold of his arm impatiently.

'Do come on, both of you. I'm frozen, and I'm dying for a glass of champagne!'

'Don't let me keep you from a party,' Francesca murmured coolly, turning her back on the little scenario to supervise the loading of her horses. 'Some of us have work to do.'

'I'll see you next Friday night, Francesca,' Saul said quietly, by way of farewell. 'Sarah and Angus are coming, too.'

'Sorry, Friday's a bad night for me,' she said breezily, not turning round. 'I'm afraid I won't be able to make it.'

* * *

It was a positive, assertive way of handling the situation, Francesca told herself as the days passed and Friday loomed closer. She had no intention of changing her mind. Not even the fact that Carol had gone over to stay with Saul at Leigh Barton, pleading with her to come and visit them whenever she could, had swayed her decision. And the infuriating twinge of disappointment she'd identified when Saul had failed to pursue the invitation, sending his groom over with the horses to be stabled, had strengthened her resolve even further.

The week flew by in a round of business matters. She met her father's solicitor, who confirmed that since the stables had been gifted to her she was liable for only a nominal portion of inheritance tax, and then astonished her with the news that he'd received an offer to buy the stables and the house as a going concern from an anonymous source, naming a sum which made her head reel.

'But who on earth is it?'

'I really can't say.' The solicitor was an old friend of her father's, slightly pompous as he stared at her solemnly beneath enormously shaggy eyebrows and over the top of half-moon spectacles. 'The offer has come via another firm of solicitors, who insist their client's name be withheld.'

Well, she wouldn't sell, she informed him calmly. She was quite determined not to sell. She might not always have wanted to devote every waking hour of her life to horses, but now that she'd come this far, brought the business this far, she'd hate to lose it. It was a kind of pride, and—loyalty, really; loyalty to her parents. Fired with fresh determination to make a huge success out of the stables purely through her own endeavours, she marched off to see the estate agents about the twenty-acre field, full of optimism, only to be told that, having received several offers, they were now requesting sealed bids with a seven-day deadline.

For the first time it dawned on her that just because that land adjoined hers, and just because she had a desperate *need* of it, it didn't necessarily follow that she was automatically going to get it. It was a sobering thought. Duly re-submitting her bid, she had to comfort herself with the fact that Doug Standish at Coombe Farm was an old family friend, and at least she'd made an offer considerably higher than the recommended guide price.

Now all she could do was wait and hope.

'Surely *you're* coming to Saul's housewarming, Chessy?' Sarah demanded, calling in for a cup of tea on the Thursday afternoon and raising her eyebrows in astonishment when Francesca announced her intention of doing the accounts on the night in question.

'No, I'm not.'

Sarah ran a hand through her tousled honey-blonde curls and made a teasing face. 'Come on, you can't be bored with parties—you hardly ever go to any! Frankly, any chance to relax and get away from the daily grind of those little darlings I teach at the village school is a bonus. I wouldn't miss it for anything!'

'I'm busy that night——'

'The whole village is talking about it,' Sarah went on, disregarding her. 'Saul's hired Rosa Venn from Church Street as a housekeeper—can you believe it?'

'Not *Rosa Venn*!' Francesca groaned, with a half-laugh. Rosa Venn was a widow of uncertain years whose reputation as an avid gossip was second only to Maggie French's at the post office. 'Poor Saul—he'll have to watch his Ps and Qs from now on, or his misdemeanours will be pinned up on the village notice-board!'

'Mmm,' Sarah's laughing hazel eyes grew more serious. 'Rosa and Maggie would bring back the stocks if they had their way. Chessy, you don't think maybe one particularly juicy source of gossip might be averted if you *went* to Saul's party, do you?'

Francesca became very still, her gaze fixed on Spike's antics with a beef-hide dog-chew he was trying desperately hard to tear to pieces with his teeth. Through the open kitchen door she could see Gina setting off out of the stableyard with a group of beginners on leading-reins.

'Don't look like that, Chessy.' Sarah put her red pottery mug down with an abrupt rattle on the old pine table and came over to put her arm around Francesca's rigid shoulders. 'I know you don't like talking about the past, but you can't play the ostrich forever. Sooner or later the questions are going to begin. Do you see what I'm driving at?'

'I'm not sure. . .' Her lips felt so stiff that it was an effort to form the words.

'I'm only saying this because of something I overheard the other day. There's already talk in the shop about you and Saul, the way you've been acting in each other's company. . .Chessy, love, I'm not suggesting for a moment there's anything to hide between you and Saul. I'm just warning you that if you openly avoid him, turn down invitations to perfectly innocuous housewarming parties and have stand-up rows with him whenever you meet, the village tongues are going to start wagging.'

Francesca said nothing. She couldn't think of anything to say. But her heart was thudding as if she'd run half a mile.

'I've known you since we were—what—six?' Sarah persisted gently.

'Something like that. . .' To ease the tension building up inside her, Francesca stood up abruptly and went to lean on the lower half of the stable-style kitchen door, staring down the hill at the disappearing string of riders, her back to her friend. She didn't want Sarah to read the writhing misery in her eyes.

'I've known Saul nearly as long,' Sarah added thoughtfully. 'Let's face it, whenever he was home from Eton the two of you were practically inseparable. You almost lived at Leigh Barton, didn't you?'

'Until he went to Oxford. Sarah, I'm sorry, I really don't want to talk about this——'

'Sorry—my fault. None of my business. Angus told me to keep my big mouth shut——'

'Angus has heard the gossip as well? You've been *discussing* me?'

'We *are* married, Chessy.' Sarah sounded slightly hurt.

'Yes, sorry. . . I didn't mean to snap. I just feel under. . .under pressure at the moment.'

'Heavens, just listen to us! Saying sorry to each other with every other word!' Sarah laughed, coming over to stand beside her at the door, her expression sobering as she took in Francesca's strained appearance, laying a hand on her arm. 'Chessy. . . I'm overstepping the mark, I know. But I'm thinking of Wenna. She is my god-daughter. She's coming up to the "Who's my daddy?" phase. It just needs one of the mothers at playgroup to say something. . . I know what it's like for children—I teach a little boy at school who comes over from another village because his mother knew he'd been getting teased at his previous school. Children can be so cruel to each other. . .'

'Sarah, please. . .just get what you want to say over and done with, will you?'

'Right. If you keep openly feuding with Saul people may jump to their own conclusions. I'd have thought you'd rather the facts were totally accurate, and that they came from you and not some Nosy Parker with nothing better to do all day than indulge in idle speculation!'

Her friend shrugged and spread her hands, making a comical face as she finished her speech. Francesca stared at her, her heart thumping, unsure whether to confide at last, unsure how much Sarah had guessed already. . .

'I'm on your side, Chessy, honestly!' The fierce loyalty in Sarah's tone made her laugh, in spite of herself. The tension abruptly eased. The moment for confidences was over.

'OK, thanks for the tip-off. I can't promise to come to this party of his, but from now on I'll be sweetness and light around my dear cousin Saul. Though how you imagine *that* will solve the problem, goodness knows.' Francesca drained her teacup and grimaced. 'In my insidious position as the "fallen woman of Bellbridge" it's hard to win, whichever way you see it!' she added lightly.

'You make yourself sound like one of Thomas Hardy's victim-heroines!' Sarah teased, rather pink in her face now that she'd found the courage to speak her mind.

But the advice echoed in Francesca's head almost continuously over the next twenty-four hours. She wasn't really aware of the moment she came to the decision to go to Saul's housewarming party after all, but by the time Friday evening came around she found herself dutifully showering and dressing, fired with a fresh sense of duty and determination.

Sarah's words had taken her by surprise, but the truth had been staring her in the face for a long time. Why on earth hadn't she been able to see it? She owed it to Lowenna, and to herself, to put things straight soon. Any question of long-term commitment was completely unthinkable, of course. But Lowenna needed the basic facts about her father, not some second-hand rumour which might give her a completely wrong idea.

She froze in the act of brushing her hair, her blood suddenly running cold at the prospect of delving into the past, trying to sort out the misunderstandings and the bitterness. The sheer immensity of it was so daunting that she wished she could gather up Lowenna and run away, go anywhere away from Bellbridge, out of range of people who thought everyone else's business was their own, but most of all, and totally irrationally, out of Saul's range and influence.

With trembling fingers she fastened the buttons on her cream silk blouse and chided herself for her melodramatic fears. One thing she'd learned during her life so far was that she was a survivor. She could cope, no matter how rough it got. And, after the rigours of the recent years, that coping would extend to something as simple, as trivial as a housewarming party at a neighbouring house, she told herself mockingly, sliding a soft, calf-length suede skirt up over her hips and fastening the small waist with a tan leather belt. Pushing her feet into matching leather court shoes and raking a couple of tortoiseshell combs through her hair to hold the heavy dark weight off her face, she stared at her reflection numbly.

Not bad, not too bad at all, she decided positively, glad of her fresh surge of confidence. An amber necklace finished off the outfit, plus some smooth amber-pink lipstick and a hint of smoky blue around her eyes. The combs held her hair off her forehead and let it hang down her back in a heavy dark curtain. The natural tawny-gold sheen of her skin had improved with the particular stage in her monthly cycle, the way it always did. Tonight she could almost be termed as radiant, something which would assist her performance quite considerably, together with her theatrical aspirations of the dim and distant past.

She'd need both if she was going to impress Rosa Venn with her casual but friendly indifference to Saul Gallagher at his housewarming party!

One thing was certain, though, she reflected, driving the short distance to Leigh Barton and approaching the familiar sprawl of the house along the oak-shaded driveway. Sarah was right about the gossips. Her problems with Saul should stay private and personal. Whatever the depth of bitterness and suspicion between them, she owed it to Lowenna not to publicise a feud with a step-cousin she'd once been openly devoted to.

It could only fuel the speculations which had undoubtedly been circulating Bellbridge ever since Lowenna Juliet St Aubyn had made her first appearance in the world one chilly April day three years ago.

CHAPTER SIX

'CHESSY, darling! Saul told me you couldn't come—
I'm so glad you could make it after all! I half expected
you to arrive with Sarah and Angus. . .'

Carol's delighted greeting softened the ordeal of
entering the crowded room alone. Francesca's aunt
kissed her warmly on the cheek, fragrant and slightly
bohemian as usual in a swirling black cotton skirt,
black blouse and Indian print shawl, her curly Titian
hair loose around her shoulders. She looked relaxed
and happy. Saul's ownership of Leigh Barton must
have evoked a lot of memories, but if she felt strange
being back in the house she'd lived in for eighteen
years with Uncle Harry she gave no sign.

Staring around the big, low-ceilinged room, with its
ancient bumpy walls and massive oak beams, Francesca
shivered as she recalled her father's fury at Leigh
Barton's sale. This, after all, had been *his* old family
home, the place where he and Harry had grown up.
The prospect of its being passed down to Saul had been
bad enough, but for it to be sold out of the family by
his brother's wife. . .

'You look dazed, my dear!' Carol smiled, a flicker of
understanding in her eyes. 'Funny how a pile of stones
and mortar can have such a powerful effect on people,
isn't it? The Romanies despise us for our attachment
to property, you know. That was one of the first things
I learned when I started living in their camps, studying
their lifestyle for that long-lost thesis of mine.'

Francesca glanced at her aunt curiously. 'Lost when you met Saul's father, you mean?'

'As good as.' Carol made a slight, rueful face. 'Jack Gallagher. . . You know, I really *loved* that man? Oh, I loved Harry as well, but Saul's father. . .'

Francesca stared at Carol, feeling that fascination with the distant past surging back unbidden. Now was hardly the time to question Carol about it, but more strongly than ever before she wanted to know what had gone wrong.

'I confess the past came rushing back for me too, the minute I stepped through this door.'

Carol nodded slowly. 'There are too many memories. . .too many shadows. Come on,' Carol's expression was suddenly firm, as if she was determined to shake off the past and enjoy the present, 'Saul's busy over there with a bunch of his polo friends—come and meet the one I've been chatting to.'

Through a haze of cigar smoke and the steady murmur of conversation, Francesca found herself steered firmly to a vantage-point by the massive inglenook, a glass of red wine in her hand, and Gabriel Andrada to make idle conversation with.

With a creeping dismay, she realised that the party was formal dress. The men wore dinner jackets, the women were in a variety of stunning taffetas and satins, low-necked and ruffled—even Sarah, she noticed out of the corner of her eye, waving as her friend spotted her and smiled across. In her cream silk blouse and longish, full suede skirt, Francesca was hardly scruffily dressed, but even so. . .

Absently replying to Gabriel's comments with a lack of attention she felt guilty about afterwards, her eyes were drawn to Saul, tall and broad-shouldered in classic

black evening suit, laughing and talking among a group
of muscled, tough-looking men and slender, suntanned
blondes, easily the most attractive man in the room.
Why on earth hadn't he told her it was formal dress?
Because she'd told him she wasn't coming, came the
small voice of reason. Her feeling of pique that he
hadn't pursued the matter a little more persistently
annoyed her so much that she thrust it out of her mind
with brutal swiftness.

'Hello there!' Charmian Baron appeared at her
shoulder, chic and composed and overpoweringly
glamorous in an emerald taffeta evening gown, low-
necked and puff-sleeved. 'Everything OK? You need a
refill—let me see to it. . .'

It took Francesca several moments to identify why
she felt illogically provoked by this helpful attention—
Saul's friend Charmian was acting the gracious hostess,
demonstrating quite clearly her close relationship with
Saul.

Gabriel, having waxed rather poetic about the
unusually dark blue shade of Francesca's eyes and the
reddish tints in her dark hair, was now holding forth at
some length about the merits of English polo professionals versus South American, and she was gazing
at him with polite attention, her thoughts elsewhere,
when Saul's deep voice interrupted.

'Don't listen to a word of this, Chessy.' Expression
guarded, he bent and brushed a kiss of greeting against
her cheek, triggering a mass of goose-pimples all over
her body. 'Gabriel's biased. He thinks only South
Americans can be natural riders. Glad you could make
it—you look stunning.'

'I feel slightly under-dressed. You might have
warned me it was dinner-jackets.'

'You told me you couldn't come.'

'I've been telling Francesca that even without the finery of a ballgown she is undoubtedly the *most* beautiful woman in the room, Saul,' the Argentinian purred, grinning from one to the other. 'The jewel in the crown. If I am biased in any direction, *amigo*, it is only towards this enchanting step-cousin of yours!'

The sociable smile on Saul's dark face grew just a touch strained. Francesca felt a twinge of annoyance, coupled with a none too honourable stab of triumph. She treated Gabriel to one of her luminous smiles, accepting the red wine proffered by the returning Charmian with commendable poise.

'I'm sure you say that to all the women you meet!' she laughed, ignoring the displeasure radiating from Saul at her side. 'But thank you anyway!'

'My pleasure, *cara*. And may I be bold? Can I ask you to come as my guest to a polo match some time this month?'

She refused to meet Saul's eyes. 'You know, I haven't been to watch polo since my Uncle Harry died. Thank you. I'd love to, Gabriel.'

'Then I am a very happy man!'

He lifted her hand to his lips, dark eyes gleaming.

'I can never work out why men play polo at all,' Charmian cut in with a husky laugh. 'All that aggression—it's quite bloodthirsty!' Her expression belied her words. Charmian looked as if she secretly revelled in the idea.

'Controlled aggression,' Saul said silkily, his eyes on Francesca. 'We play polo to vent violent feelings in a way which doesn't get us locked up in the police station.'

'Really?' Francesca queried, her eyes wide. 'So

you're saying that thundering around on the polo field keeps a lot of hot-blooded males from serious criminal assault charges?'

'Possibly.' Saul's voice held a steely undertone. His smile was for appearances only. 'Would you excuse us?' he went on, taking her arm in a grip which brooked no argument. 'I promised Francesca I'd show her over the house—she and I used to play here together as children, so nostalgia rules the day. . .'

Briefly glimpsing the frozen smile on Charmian's lips, she was whisked out of the room with a speed which strained decorum, and propelled into the nearest empty room which happened to be the rear conservatory, warm and slightly steamy from the masses of lush green foliage.

With the back of his heel Saul kicked the door shut behind them.

'This is very pleasant,' she began flippantly, gazing around at the jungle of leaves and beyond through the glass to the chequered acres of farmland. 'You've been busy getting the place straight so quickly——'

'Charmian's been doing it. . .'

'Ah, yes.' The car-phone-using Daihatsu-driving blonde had now been well and truly identified, Francesca thought with a twinge of hysteria welling up inside her. Saul's live-in lover, who'd been entrusted with the important task of preparing his new country retreat for his arrival. 'Well, it all looks very smart——'

'I didn't march you in here to make idle social chit-chat about decorations and house-moving problems. . .'

'I gathered that! What on earth's the matter?' she demanded, facing him warily. Her heart was thudding heavily against her breastbone. 'You're supposed to be a civilised, well-educated man, remember? You've got a first-class honours degree in Humanities at Oxford; so why the caveman act?'

Saul crossed the conservatory until he was standing a mere two inches away from her, staring down into her face with a glitter of unholy amusement creeping into his eyes. Reaching out, he took hold of her shoulders, drawing her towards him until the breath seemed to rush out of her in utter panic.

'You'd like me to appear civilised and well-educated, would you? OK—*nemo me impune lacessit*,' Saul murmured with a quirk of a smile at the corner of his mouth, his hands slamming her abruptly against him so that she caught her breath involuntarily.

'I didn't ask you to quote obscure Latin proverbs at me!' she countered shakily, her voice infuriatingly husky. 'What the hell does that mean?'

'It means, my beautiful little step-cousin, "No one provokes me with impunity".'

'Very erudite. Am I supposed to be bowled over by your academic brilliance?'

'In a way.' He tightened his grip on her, raising the temperature between them to an almost unbearable degree. 'I was always prepared to go to any lengths to prove to you I wasn't the rough, illiterate gypsy-boy your father branded me.'

His voice had altered, roughened. It was impossible to tell what was going on in his mind. That closed, shuttered way he had of masking his true feelings was never more evident. There was suppressed fury there, but she could feel the hardening evidence of his desire as he crushed her relentlessly to the braced tension of his thighs.

She should be fighting, an appalled, far-off voice was reminding her. This was insane. . .

A wave of fiery warmth was creeping up from her thighs to her neck. Her knees were stubbornly dissolving.

'Aren't you going to ask me to let go of you?' The last few words were breathed against her mouth, and with a massive shock she felt the touch of Saul's mouth on hers, the extraordinarily sensual taste of his tongue gaining entry between her parted lips. With a muffled moan she opened to his kiss, feathers of awareness sensitising her body from top to toe, from breast to groin, draining her brain totally. He tasted so good; even the smell of him was so right, some indescribable mix of clean, warm skin and spicy musk cologne. . .

Time stood still, then seemed to tilt, rush backwards, the vivid past springing to life, with all the pain and pleasure somehow indistinguishable from one another. Convulsing helplessly against him, she felt him tense, then withdraw from her slightly, leaving her stunned and frustrated and thoroughly outraged by the strength of her own treacherous emotions. Holding her at arm's length, his hands on her shoulders, he stared at her quietly, his eyes unfathomable.

'Saul. . .' It was a choked whisper. 'Why did you do that?'

'Curiosity. I wanted to bring back a few memories.'

'Saul. . .'

'Are you hungry?' The cool grey eyes were pitiless as they scanned her hot face and flicked ruthlessly down the length of her slender form.

'No! I'm not at all hungry——'

'No?' The double-edged meaning was remorseless.

'Then shall we look over the house? Relive those happy summer vacations when we played here?'

'No! Saul, I——'

'What's wrong, Francesca? Don't you like reliving the past?'

Their eyes clashed and held, stormy dark blue with glacier-grey. They stared at each other in savage silence, Saul dangerously cool and elegant in formal attire, Francesca taut as a reed, scarcely aware of the painful grip of his fingers on her shoulders. His eyes were moving over her body, to linger on the rapid rise and fall of her breasts. Their peaks were aching, taut, straining against the soft fabric of the satin camisole under her blouse. Humiliation rushed over her like a tidal wave as she saw the glint of triumphant knowledge in his eyes.

'Don't you want to satisfy your curiosity again, Chessy?'

'Stop it!'

'I'm only looking. You still wear no bra. . . Those beautiful breasts of yours still support themselves.' His voice was a husky mockery, but ragged with desire, his eyes darker, the pupils dilating slightly as he scrutinised her. She was trembling now, violently, and to her chagrin hot, angry tears were pricking her eyelids. With a sudden, muffled oath Saul pulled her back into his arms, holding her hard against his chest, pressing her cheek to the lapel of his jacket, his thumb stroking the tears which were wetting her face and his shirt at the same time.

To her horror she couldn't stop crying once she'd started. Great shuddering sobs racked her. She'd no idea so much emotion was choked inside her.

'Sorry. . . I *hate* crying. . .'

'Oh, Chessy. . .' Saul's voice was unrecognisable; remorse and self-contempt mingled with the pity she thought she detected. Stiffening, she tried to wriggle free but he held on to her, his fingers stroking her hair, his body heat providing the physical comfort she needed. 'It's good to cry. Didn't you know that?'

'No, it's not. It gives you a headache. Makes your eyes red and swollen.'

'Come and sit down.' He sounded abrupt, steering her to the white wrought-iron bench in the corner. 'Damn—I'm sorry. You're still getting over your father's death. I'm putting emotional pressure on you.'

In silence, she sank down on to the bench, feeling the cooler ironwork through the thin fabric of her blouse, taking the proffered white handkerchief Saul had fished out of his pocket and wiping her eyes.

'No, it's not you,' she said at last, her voice as light as she could make it, 'and it's not even my father's death. I had long enough to come to terms with that, knowing he was dying for three years.'

'It's still a shock when it happens.'

'Yes, I know. But tonight. . . I think it's thrown me being here again.' And being held in Saul's arms again, kissing him again. . . The silent admission made the panic grow even stronger.

'I thought you loved this house.' His voice was flat. Sitting down on the bench beside her, he stretched out his long legs and stared expressionlessly at the polished toes of his patent dress shoes.

'I did. I do.' She stared out of the glass conservatory, absorbing the tranquil beauty of the Devon countryside around her, the shadows just beginning to lengthen on this glorious May evening. The hills were blurring into a soft pale grey mist. In another sweeping green pasture four of Saul's exquisite thoroughbreds suddenly broke into a joyous gallop—a chestnut, a grey and two bays. Manes and tails streaming behind them, they scattered towards the distant birch wood where a soft mauve carpet of bluebells coloured the ground.

Taking a deep breath, she managed to control her see-saw emotions. With a passable attempt at a smile, she added, 'Some of the happiest moments of my life have been spent in this house. Whenever you were home for vacations, my parents hardly saw me at Hill Mead!'

'I seem to remember a lot of galloping around on horseback, playing pirates in the orchard, or occasionally being forced into dressing up for your fairy stories!' Saul wasn't smiling. 'I was fonder of the pirates and the horse-riding games, as I recall.'

'Mmm. You weren't keen on my theatrical productions. . .' The colour in her cheeks rose slightly as she remembered one of her favourite fantasies, a scenario she'd insisted on acting out on numerous occasions after finding an old spinning-wheel up in the dusty attics. Saul had promptly been cast as the handsome prince, with herself in the role of Sleeping Beauty. Problems had invariably arisen because the derisive fourteen-year-old Saul had frequent left an irate ten-year-old 'sleeping' in the attics for an indefinite period while he disappeared to find a game more to his taste. . .

'All my memories are of playing here at Leigh Barton,' she said slowly as the silence between them lengthened again. 'It's funny, I can't recall any games at Hill Mead.'

'That's because I was *persona non grata* at Hill Mead most of the time——'

'Oh, Saul!' She turned uncertainly, trying to read his eyes. 'It wasn't that bad.'

He gave a short, low laugh at her expression. 'Don't look so worried. I haven't finished up with a permanent chip on my shoulder. Rejection—persecution in certain quarters—probably made me more. . .arrogant?' He smiled with a trace of self-mockery. 'It took that year travelling with my real father to convince me I wasn't some sort of superior being from a vastly superior race! Romany customs turned out to have just as many injustices and prejudices as Gorgio customs. . . *My* fantasy hero turned out to have clay feet.'

'Brave of you to be so frank,' she murmured wryly.

'Oh, I've many faults but lack of courage isn't one of them,' Saul said softly, his grey eyes suddenly narrowing on her face. 'How about you, Chessy? Do you lack courage?'

She stared at him, her throat constricting. She wished she knew what he was getting at. 'I don't know. Physically, do you mean?'

'Physically, you've a lot of courage. You couldn't have put Vengeance at those jumps last Saturday if you hadn't. . . How about moral courage?'

She stared through the glass, her fingers clenched tensely in her lap, red flags of colour along her cheekbones. He knew. . . She'd wondered, now she was almost certain.

'Nothing to say? Do you know what intrigues me, Chessy? Did Lowenna's father just walk out and leave you to cope on your own, or didn't he ever have the chance to redeem himself? Can it be that you never told him?'

Slowly, she turned to meet his piercing gaze, blinking slightly at the dazzling glint of cold anger in his eyes.

'Maybe I just never knew who the father was,' she suggested with studied insolence, wishing her voice didn't hold that choked tremor of emotion.

'Lowenna needs a father. Being clever and fashionable and so-called liberated is no compensation for giving a child a secure family life——'

'There's nothing clever and fashionable about getting pregnant when you don't intend getting pregnant!' She saw the flicker in Saul's eyes, and felt heat rushing up to her hairline, and added bitterly, 'But then, after all, it was all my own fault, wasn't it? Because as you pointed out at the time I *was* rather indiscriminate with my favours!'

'Francesca. . .' Saul's face darkened; his voice had deepened with distaste.

'What's wrong now? Moral courage is daring to speak the truth, isn't it? And, let's face it, you *knew* the situation four years ago, didn't you? It was you who spelt it out to me with such unforgettable *tact* and *diplomacy* at the time!'

She stood up, and Saul followed, towering over her, his eyes almost black with the sudden onslaught of fury. Dusk was falling and the lights from the main house were spilling bright yellow pools on to the surrounding terraces, isolating them in the dark, humid intimacy of the conservatory.

'Let me see if I can recollect the exact scenario, shall I?' Saul grated harshly. 'It has all the elements of classic farce, if my memory serves me well. You're supposed to be getting engaged to Julian Harrington-Green on your eighteenth birthday. For most of the party you're flirting outrageously with every available male, with the notable exception of the said Julian Harrington-Green. *I* then find you in a compromising situation in the stables with Neville Beresford.' He paused, his eyes remorseless. 'Do I have this right so far?'

'Are you ever wrong?' Bitter sarcasm hid the furious anguish she was damming down inside her.

'So Beresford beats a hasty retreat, I find myself trying to console you, the devil only knows for what reason, then in marches your father, and all hell lets loose. The next day, you turn up in *my* hotel bedroom, still playing your little games, and when the game changes you're all aggrieved innocence——'

'And *you're* the thickest-skinned, stupidest man I know!' she burst out, rigid with indignation. 'Did you say travelling with your real father cured you of your arrogance? Because you're fooling yourself! You're the most arrogant, self-opinionated male I've ever met; you think you're some kind of god; your pomposity and self-righteousness *nauseate* me——'

'Oh, dear. . .' a husky voice with a trace of amusement cut in through the sudden, appalled silence following this diatribe '. . . I seem to have barged in at a rather embarrassing moment. I'm so sorry.' Charmian's brown eyes weren't at all sorry: they were hard as conkers as she flicked them from Francesca's flushed cheeks to the chalk-white mask of Saul's face. 'Saul, darling, phone call for you. Alfie Cavendish about next Thursday.'

'Tell him I'll ring him back.' The steel in Saul's voice had a whiplash fury which made even Charmian wince.

'But Saul——'

'Don't bother on my account. . .' Francesca pushed past them both and headed for the door, gaining her freedom and running swiftly towards the stairs, anxious to gain the sanctuary of one of the upper bathrooms.

The puffy, stinging feeling in her eyes told her she was in no state to rejoin the rest of the elegant guests in the sitting-room. She had to find somewhere she could sit and think and be alone. Saul's vitriolic words had triggered a terrible sense of anxiety inside her. Everything that had happened in her life so far, all the lonely decisions she'd made over the last four traumatic years—it all seemed even more confusing and alarming and damning than ever.

Someone had decorated the bathroom in the height of the latest 'good taste'. A beautifully restored white suite, mahogany fittings, rich and slightly faded-looking brocade patterned wallpaper and curtains. . . Charmian Baron's choices, she told herself masochistically, staring miserably into the mirror as she splashed cold water over her eyes and tried to restore some modicum of composure to her expression.

How could Saul allow a woman like Charmian free rein to redecorate this lovely old house? It was obviously a sign of the depth of his feelings for her. A sickness was churning in the pit of her stomach. How could she be so stupid? How could she allow herself to feel jealous of the woman in Saul's life? That kind of lacerating self-indulgence could only end in despair. . .

How Francesca came to be retreating up to the attics she wasn't sure. But the memory of the stillness, the secret isolation of those dusty old rooms, was like a silent ghost, luring her upwards. Footsteps echoing on the bare floorboards, she walked silently from room to room, shivering slightly in the cool gloom. It was all different, of course. The junk she remembered from her childhood had gone, replaced by a new set of junk. Although when she opened the last door she was surprised to see one or two vaguely familiar items.

Presumably the last two owners hadn't had the time or the inclination to sort through it all. Here, amazingly, was the dusty old spinning-wheel, hemmed in by rolled-up carpets, old curtains, piles of discarded paintings, face to the wall. The ancient chaise-longue with its broken back and worn green velvet cover still stood against the far end. . .

'I used to leave you up here, playing your acting games.' Saul's soft voice behind her made her jump so violently that her heart lurched painfully in her chest. 'I used to go riding, or go fishing in the stream sometimes. Those ten-year-old tantrums you used to fly into when I finally showed up were very entertaining!'

Spinning round, she stared at him angrily. In the half-dusk his skin looked very dark and swarthy against the ice-white of his dress shirt.

'Leave me alone, Saul. . .'

'What are you doing up here?'

'Thinking,' she snapped shakily. 'Trying to find somewhere I can be *alone*!'

'I thought you'd run out on me again. I checked to see if your car had gone.' He stepped closer, the quietness of his tread ominous in itself. The tiny hairs all over her body were standing on end in her sudden shiver of fright. 'Then I had a sixth sense I might find you up here.'

'Saul, if you touch me again I'll. . .'

'You'll what?' he mocked softly, reaching her and cupping her white face in his hands. 'Scream? Run downstairs and ring your WPC friend? Is she a fellow women's libber who thinks all men are rapists?'

'Stop it!'

'Oh, no, not this time.' The soft, brutal whisper was

against her ear, and without warning she was lifted off
her feet and savagely spread-eagled on the chaise-
longue. 'We've done enough talking, Chessy. . .
enough fencing. You've called me enough rude names
to last a lifetime. . . Let's have another go at that
favourite "Sleeping Beauty" game of yours, shall we?
The difference this time is I don't think kissing girls is
silly any more. . .'

'Let me *go!*' Her furious struggles were proving a
complete waste of energy. With humiliating ease, Saul
pinned her to the sofa and covered her protesting
mouth with his, pressing his hard length against her
writhing body and caressing her shoulders, her ribs,
her waist, her hips with long, calming, inexplicably
arousing movements which made her cry out in an
anguish of fear and outrage.

'I'll let you go when you've admitted you want me as
much as I want you. . .'

'No, never. . .'

'No?' The shadows threw the harsh face above her
into stark relief, as Saul drew slightly back, his thighs
holding her immobile as he began to unbutton her
blouse, sliding his fingers inside with bold expertise as
he did so, then peeling the camisole up to expose the
pale glimmer of her breasts, swelling tautly up towards
him, the nipples rosy brown nubs, aching to be stroked.
'No?' he repeated hoarsely, lowering his head to flick
his tongue gently across the stiff peak of one breast and
watching her flinch in an agony of suppressed desire.
'Where's all that moral courage now, Chessy? The
courage to speak the truth?'

'You're a loathsome. . .conceited. . .bully!' she
managed to whisper raggedly, clenching her hands at
her sides to stop herself from wrapping her arms

around him, from clutching him hungrily down to her and melting beneath him. 'You're taking advantage of one silly mistake. . .'

'Which of us made the mistake? Which of us changed the rules of the game, Chessy?' The warm tongue moved across to the other breast and she sucked in her breath unevenly, aware that her stomach was hot with desire, that her legs had become boneless beneath Saul's muscled weight.

'Saul. . .stop this, I beg you. . .'

'You *beg* me?' He was giving no quarter, grasping her wrists and pinning them back above her head, his mouth rising from her breasts to the pulse which was beating rapidly at the base of her neck. 'Shall I tell you your latest mistake? Coming to my party tonight to flirt with my good friend Gabriel Andrada, who, I can assure you, is always only too happy to oblige a lady in any capacity she cares to choose——'

'Don't talk rubbish, Saul—no! This isn't. . .we can't just. . .'

'Yes, we can. . .oh, yes. . .' His voice had thickened, coarsened. His caressing hands grew bolder, discovering the secret places which triggered a mindless, frantic yearning no other person had ever discovered. . .

A blackness was filling her mind, growing and growing until there was a pulsing fire in the blackness, a great void yawning and vulnerable inside her. Suddenly there was no point in protesting, no point in thinking. . .all the scattered bits of her shredded emotions kaleidoscoped together, erasing her confusion. Everything was briefly uncomplicated as the long empty vacuum of the last four years crashed to an abrupt end.

'I want you, Chessy. . .' It was a husky, sensual groan against her lips, bringing a short, bitter laugh from her as she shivered under his fingers. 'I've never stopped wanting you. . .'

'Saul. . .'

'Tell me the truth. . .you want me too?'

'Oh, yes. . .but I wish I didn't. . .' It was a broken sob of admission, lost in the mounting demand of his kiss.

'Oh, lord. . . Chessy, Chessy. . .' His skilful fingers had slid open zips and buttons, dispensed with her skirt. Passion took over. No use denying it. Shuddering, both of them blind and deaf with impatience, they clasped each other with fierce hunger, lips and bodies tangling. The mounting sensation in her pelvis made her cry out with mingled pleasure and anger. She could feel Saul's taut control, sense the suppression of powerful sensuality he was withholding—like flood-water behind a weakening dam. The cool air of the room was briefly on her naked thighs before the shock of Saul's warm, hair-roughened body covered her, and in a sudden ferocious act of possession he'd separated her legs to force a place for himself there.

And then, with devastating clarity, she came to her senses. Not again. . .not again; the words screamed at her silently. She might have been foolish once, but not again. . . The crazy excitement gripping her wasn't enough to wipe out the memories of the last four years, the pain and anguish. . .the bitter-sweet chemistry between herself and this one man wasn't enough. . .

Sheer terror gave her the strength to double up beneath Saul's weight, to fight him with every ounce of muscle she could revive. Gasping with fear and anger, she thrashed violently to free herself.

And then, abruptly, she was released. It was over. Exhausted, damp with perspiration, limp as a rag doll in spite of the ache of frustration in her groin, she lay on the chaise-longue, aware that Saul had almost instantly been smitten with appalled remorse.

The silence in the shadowy attic was so thick that she felt as if the ghosts could emerge from the peeling walls, walk around them without fear of human presence. She wished passionately that she could die, join that invisible throng. . .anything to escape Saul's dark, haunted eyes as he stared at her grimly in the half-light.

'I was afraid to come tonight. . .now I see why.' She forced herself to sit up, began a fumbling search for items of clothing tossed anyhow around them at the height of their passion.

'Why be afraid?' Saul's deep voice was ragged, a wry note of self-mockery discernible. 'Your "virtue" is still intact, Francesca, even though you wanted that as much as I did.' His breathing was still faster than normal.

'Oh, I *wanted* it! That doesn't make me *like* what happened! It doesn't make me like you, either, or myself.'

'Francesca, I'm sorry——'

'You're sorry? Why did you do it, Saul?'

There was a long, charged silence. Saul sat up, began to drag on his clothes with an air of self-recrimination about his movements.

'Let's say I had in mind to persuade you to be *my* guest at any polo match you might be planning on watching?' he said, his voice heavy with sarcasm.

'Are you *serious*?' She could hardly believe they were having this conversation, that they'd just lain together on that chaise-longue with a degree of abandon she'd never have dreamed possible in a thousand years of dreaming about it. . .

'Never more so. Now you see the extent of my regrettably jealous nature. . .'

'I can't believe I'm hearing this, Saul! You're jealous of Gabriel, just because he asked me to go to a polo match with him? Yet you left that day, fours years ago—you just left, without a word. . .and you've stayed away all this time!'

'Everything was a shambles,' Saul said in a slow, angry-sounding voice, as if it were somehow entirely her fault that everything had been a shambles. 'When I came back for your eighteenth birthday party, I confess I was knocked sideways at the change in you. I'd been away at university, then spent that six months with my father. From being a tomboyish little fifteen, you'd blossomed into a desirable woman. I was. . .shattered by how much I *wanted* you, Chessy! It felt. . .indecent. Incestuous. When you came to my hotel room the day afterwards, I'd spent one hell of a night, lying awake smoking and drinking and thinking about you. . .how you'd feel, how you'd respond if I had you there in my bed with me——'

'But you just disappeared, Saul!'

'We both had things to sort out.'

'Don't you mean you'd satisfied your curiosity about how your little step-cousin would feel if you took her to bed with you, and it was time to seek pastures new again?'

'No.' Saul sounded hunted. 'There was your father to take into account, damn it——'

'Come on, Saul! Courage to tell the truth, remember? You saw me, you fancied me, and you thought you might as well have me since you'd decided that half Bellbridge appeared to already have had the pleasure!'

'Francesca!' It was an uneven groan, so deeply anguished that she almost felt he might be sincere. 'Francesca, lord help me, how can I ever explain how you affected me? How you still affect me?'

She'd got her clothes back together. Shakily she stood up. 'Don't bother. I'll tell you exactly how I affect you.' She said icily, 'You always saw me as your devoted little cousin. Like one of your possessions. You came back from university and from your spell as a make-believe Romany to find I'd grown into a bigger cousin, apparently less devoted, apparently "flirting with men" as you put it. You wanted to remind me who was boss. Brand me with your own mark of possession. Only then you felt disgusted with yourself for transferring all those *brotherly* feelings into pure, straightforward *lust*! You said just now it felt incestuous. That's how you've always seen it, haven't you? That morning in your hotel room disgusted you. You left and went away and stayed away. Because you really didn't want to face up to, or else you *couldn't* face up to *my* feelings about *you*!'

'Quite a speech.' Saul was leaning back on the chaise-longue, watching her with bleak, haunted eyes. 'Some of it is even partly true.'

'Of course it is!' She felt so choked, the pain was suddenly so great she couldn't bear it any longer. 'You were totally self-absorbed. You never gave a damn about my feelings. And now history has almost repeated itself! But don't get too self-satisfied. All you've proved is that there's a. . .a kind of sexual attraction between us. So what? You needn't think it gives you any rights over me. I'll go to a polo match with Gabriel if I damn well want to. If you don't like it, you've got the accommodating Charmian to cheer you up! Goodnight, Saul.' She made it to the door on legs which felt full of cotton wool. 'I wish I hadn't let myself be talked into coming to your housewarming party tonight. Don't worry—I'll see myself out!'

CHAPTER SEVEN

'JUST a minute.' Saul was on his feet, barring
Francesca's exit. He switched on the light, flooding the
shadowy attic with harsh, blinding light from a naked
overhead bulb. There was dust on his dinner-jacket,
dust on her clothes. . . With an inward groan she
imagined the reaction if anyone saw them. . . '*Who*
talked you into coming tonight?'

'I—Sarah. My friend Sarah McLaren.'

The pale gaze was narrowing to its normal laser-
sharpness. 'And precisely how did she manage to
succeed where I failed, Francesca?'

With a long, slow expulsion of breath, she lifted her
chin squarely, raking a hand through her dishevelled
hair. This wasn't a good time to be courageous and tell
the truth, but it seemed to Francesca then that there
was never going to be a good time. This moment, with
all its numerous shortcomings, was going to have to
do.

'Apparently there was gossip in the village. . .' Her
voice was husky. She cleared her throat.

'Gossip?'

'About the way I was behaving around you. People
might start jumping to conclusions, putting two and
two together making whatever they chose.'

'I see.'

'Do you?' Suddenly the years of pent-up anger
seemed to come tumbling out. She faced him, blue
eyes blazing. 'I doubt it! You can have no idea what

it's like, being the object of everyone's "sympathy" and then gradually becoming the object of everyone's outright curiosity. My father's illness meant I was morally bound to stay at Hill Mead. I couldn't take my baby and go away somewhere I could be anonymous. If you have a problem in a tiny country village like Bellbridge, people rally round to help at first, but then they feel as if they've a right to pry into every aspect of your life. You become "their" property—if I go for a meal with a male friend, there are ripples of reaction for weeks afterwards! I've been the target for quite an interesting range of human emotions—sympathy, curiosity, and a fair amount of malicious scandalmongering. . .'

She stopped for breath, aware of Saul's deadpan expression intent on her flushed face, and added raggedly, 'What do you think your new housekeeper Mrs Venn would make of it if she saw me emerging from these attics in this state, covered in dust, my hair all over the place?'

'She'd probably assume you'd just been ravished on the chaise-longue.' Saul's voice was back to its habitual mocking drawl.

She glared at him irately. 'It's no joke, Saul.'

'No, absolutely no joke at all. . .but at least we weren't caught *in flagrante delicto*. . .or perhaps *in flagrante bello* might be more appropriate. "While war is raging"?'

'Spare me your clever little Latin phrases!'

'At least they're brief, apt and coherent. Which is more than can be said for your ranting and raving, Chessy.' He murmured laconically, 'What, precisely, are you trying to tell me?'

Loathing the flicker of amusement in his eyes, and suppressing a reprehensible desire to hit him, she added through clenched teeth, 'For Lowenna's sake I can't afford to be seen in compromising situations!'

'Your reputation is at stake,' Saul agreed expressionlessly.

'Yes.' It was no good; she couldn't go through with it. She'd thought she could tell him but despair surged through her, and she took a step towards the door, avoiding his mocking gaze. 'Let me pass, please. . .'

'Of course.' Saul didn't move. Something in the grey eyes made her blood boil even more. 'Should we creep down separately, so no one suspects we've been up here together?'

'It's not *funny*, Saul! I have to run the gamut of village opinion every single day of my life! My livelihood could even depend on it! My pupils' mothers will be quick to switch riding schools if they catch a whiff of further scandal about me. . .'

'Don't you think you're being slightly paranoid?'

'I don't know, but if people start spreading rumours about you and me——' She stopped, hesitating, watching the wary glitter of response in his eyes.

'They might assume that *I* could be Lowenna's father?' Saul finished up for her blandly.

There was a resounding silence. The colour drained from Francesca's face.

Suddenly Saul looked like a predatory animal, quietly, cold-bloodedly regarding its prey.

The attic room seemed to have grown unbearably quiet. She could hear faint sounds of the party far below, a murmur of voices, sudden distant bursts of laughter. Her own uneven breathing and the panic-filled drumming of her heart were nearer to hand.

'Well?' The expression on Saul's face was so bleakly accusing that she shivered inside. 'Do tell me,

Francesca; I'm surprisingly interested to know. Is there even the remotest chance that those village gossips could be right?'

The effort to speak seemed so great, she felt almost dizzy with the struggle. But pride came to her rescue; the bitter, deep-seated resentment that had kept her silent for so long.

With a slight, imperceptible shrug, she nodded. 'Yes. Since you're so interested to know, Saul.' Turning away, she walked across the bare wooden floor and went to the window, staring into the darkness outside. She could see Saul's tall, motionless figure, standing by the door as if turned to stone.

'Lowenna is *my* child?'

She had to fight with her temper. This wasn't the time to fly off the handle again. If she was to retain her dignity, it was vital she stay calm. . .

'You are telling me Lowenna is my daughter, Francesca?' The steely note was all she needed to hear. Her heart plummeted. The times she'd imagined this moment, the times she'd rehearsed it in her head, lying sleepless in her bed, or cuddling the tiny dark-haired baby in the exhausted, small hours of the morning, feeding her or trying desperately to rock her off to sleep. . .

In three fierce strides Saul had crossed the room to grasp her shoulder, spinning her round to face him. The ashen mask of his face was terrifying.

'Are you going to ask how you can be sure?' she demanded shakily, her smile a bitter parody of amusement. 'How you can be certain my baby wasn't fathered by Julian, or Anton, or Neville?' She spat the names at him with quiet fury. 'Well, you can't be sure of course.

With a girl of my "easy virtue", you'll always have your doubts.'

'Francesca, for the love of heaven. . .' He gave her a slight shake, his eyes dark hollows in his face. 'Why didn't you tell me?'

'Because you wouldn't have believed me.'

'Chessy. . .'

'You were capable of accusing me of sleeping around with all those boyfriends! You were so determined to think the worst of me! Even if it hadn't been for that row with my father, you were the *last* person I wanted to tell. . .if you were too pig-headed to see you were the only man I'd ever gone to bed with——'

'*What*?'

'See? I knew you wouldn't believe me. It doesn't matter, anyway. It must be obvious even to a half-wit that I'm not making any demands on Lowenna's father! Believe what you like. I just thought it was time to speak the "courageous truth"!'

Saul's hands fell away from her shoulders. He was staring at her as if he was seeing her, properly, for the first time.

She stared back, unsure suddenly how she felt inside. Empty, she decided. Empty and deflated. The secret was no secret any more, and letting go of it had given her no personal satisfaction whatsoever. Beginning to shiver slightly, she turned away and began to walk to the door.

'I'm going home.'

'I'll drive you.' Saul sounded stiff and restrained. Reaching the door together, he held it open for her, and a brief glance into his face confirmed her worst fears. Saul was bleakly furious. The frosty glitter in his eyes chilled her to the bone.

'I can drive myself!'

'You're in no state to drive. Come on.'

Her shivering was annoying her, but somehow she couldn't stop. Shock, emotional tension. . .whatever it was, her legs felt infuriatingly shaky, and she knew Saul was sufficiently perceptive to see it. 'What about my Land Rover?'

'I'll drive it. I'll take one of my horses from your stable and ride back.'

'Saul, if we go out together, people will——'

'I don't give a monkey's what people will think!' he ground out viciously, escorting her down the stairs and across the square, panelled hall. As luck would have it, the only person they passed was Rosa Venn, who glanced out of the kitchen door, noted their dusty, dishevelled appearance and raised her eyebrows in a fashion which augured ill for Francesca's standing in the village shop tomorrow morning.

'Thank you very much!' she grated furiously as Saul thrust her into the passenger seat of her Land Rover and took over the wheel. 'Now this will be broadcast over most of East Devon by nine-thirty a.m.!'

'So what? Everyone's going to know we're getting married, Francesca. A little forerunner to the gossip won't make any difference, one way or another!'

'Getting *married*?' she exploded, rounding on him incredulously. 'Are you *quite* mad?'

'I've never been more sane in my life.' He braked savagely outside Hill Mead, glancing up at the dark bedroom windows. 'That's my child asleep up there. I've been deprived of the first three years of her life; I'm damned if I'll be deprived of any more! In hell's name, if I'd known Lowenna was mine I wouldn't have tiptoed around making anonymous bids for Hill

Mead—I'd have slammed straight in with an offer you couldn't refuse!'

Francesca went very still. Her heart was hammering hectically. 'It was *you*?' she said at last, in a voice not quite like her own, resentment and anger warring for space inside her. 'You're the anonymous bidder for Hill Mead?'

'Yes.' Saul's glance at her in the darkness was shuttered, his voice ominously calm. 'I am. Only now the offer is extended, Francesca! I'll take over the whole operation, and that includes Miss Francesca St Aubyn and her daughter Lowenna!'

'Saul, I don't think you quite understand.' She spoke with the clear deliberation used to get the attention of the slow-witted. 'Lowenna and I are not for sale. Hill Mead Stables is not for sale. And as for getting married—marriage needs to be a mutual agreement. Relationships can only succeed through. . .through mutual understanding, valuing the other person, sharing emotional support. Getting me pregnant and then disappearing for four years does not give you the right to march me to a church at gun-point!'

'Oh, lord. . .Chessy. . .' Saul sounded deadly tired suddenly. 'Go to bed. We'll talk about this tomorrow.'

It was on the tip of her tongue to retort sharply, to tell him that she wasn't about to take orders from anyone, that she had no intention of talking about it tomorrow. . .but fatigue suddenly descended on her like a black cloak. Saul had climbed down and come round to her door, letting her out and helping her down from the vehicle with a gentle restraint totally at odds with the chilling anger of his speech, and the merciless glint in his eyes.

Before he loped off towards the stables, he watched

her open the front door and waited a second until she'd switched on the light. She briefly thought he was going to bend and kiss her, but he just gazed at her for a moment, his expression guarded.

'Goodnight, Francesca.'

'Goodnight, Saul.'

They parted with such formality that the whole fraught episode seemed like a bad dream. Francesca rapidly prepared for bed, hating her trembling hands and churning stomach. She felt angry and disturbed and somehow—somehow subtly threatened, even though there was no logical way Saul could force himself into their lives.

Before she collapsed into her bed, she crept into Lowenna's room and gazed at the pale, peaceful face of her three-year-old daughter just visible in the muted night-light.

There was something strangely emotive about a sleeping child. Her daughter slept soundly, flat on her back, hair still in two dark plaits, head on one side, one arm bent at the elbow and lying palm upwards on the pillow beside her.

Her turmoil forgotten for a few moments, Francesca gazed silently, taking in every tiny detail. There was a faint, warm perfume of bubble-bath and talcum powder. The child's breathing was light and even, the circle of dark lashes throwing shadows on the pale bloom of her cheeks. The small fingers were slightly curled, the thumb beside her mouth still wet where she'd sucked her thumb in her sleep.

Crouching down beside the bed, she had an over-powering longing to cuddle the small body in her arms, and instead clutched her arms round her knees and rested her head against the Paddington Bear quilt, still shivering in her long, flower-sprigged cotton nightdress.

How *dared* Saul be so arrogant—coming back to Bellbridge with his patronising wealth, offering to *buy* everything she had, even her freedom? Tears were welling in her eyes and silently sliding down her cheeks.

Why was she crying? she asked herself impatiently. Lowenna's existence had brought nothing but joy into her life. The love she felt for this small, unique creation held an almost reverent quality. How could anything so adorable, so perfect in every way, emerge from such bitter conflict?

No, not entirely bitter conflict. Tonight's dangerous new truthfulness was stirring all kinds of unwelcome facts to life, she reflected with wry misery. She might detest Saul Gallagher at this moment with a ferocity which alarmed her slightly, but her feelings for Saul had once been very similar to these magical, over-whelmingly joyous feelings for Lowenna.

She'd lived for Saul. When he was away at school, life had seemed drab and grey. When he came home, the world had sprung into glorious Technicolor again. Had he ever known how much she'd missed him when he went away to university? Everything seemed to have conspired at the same time to make life unbearable, make her father impossible to live with: her mother's tragic death, Dad's bitterness and fury over the sale of the St Aubyn family home—even though Francesca felt sure he'd rather it was sold than see Saul inherit it in due course.

She hadn't dared tell her father about her wavering ambitions, her secret yen to study drama. He had wanted her to make riding and horses her sole career. More to the point, he had wanted her to help him run

Hill Mead. He'd wanted to feel she was there to continue his hard work in the future. He had expected her to be like her mother, who'd lived and breathed horses to the exclusion of much else. And he'd wanted her to marry Julian Harrington-Green, link the two families, consolidate his position. . .

When Saul had come back to Bellbridge for her eighteenth birthday party, she'd seen his return in the light of a White Knight to her rescue. And then everything had gone wrong with Saul, too. . . With a silent groan she recalled that ghastly night. Desperate unhappiness had made her behave badly at her party. She'd crimped her long dark hair and worn it down in a wild cascade around her shoulders, worn more make-up than usual, borrowed one of Sarah's most daring dresses, a tight strapless affair with a boned bodice and a slit reaching halfway up the thigh, in brilliant pea-cock-blue. Being rather better endowed in the bust than her friend, she'd caused something of a stir among the male guests, she flinched from recalling. It had been a hot July and she'd spent a few weekends down at the beach. The dress had revealed an awful lot of golden brown flesh. . .

And then Saul had walked in, tall and dark and powerful-looking, a man rather than a boy, dressed in black from head to toe in polo-neck and cords, gold gypsy earrings and collar-length gypsy-black hair, making every girl in the room swivel her neck to stare. He'd shrugged off the female attention with the prac-tised ease of comparative maturity. Those four years between them had never seemed such a chasm. And suddenly it hadn't been enough to rebel against the cold-blooded matchmaking with Julian by flirting with every boy she danced with. She'd wanted Saul to dance with her, she'd wanted Saul to come and talk to her, stay at her side, bridge the gap which now seemed to yawn between them. . .

She got to her feet, stiff and aching with tiredness, bending to kiss the sleeping child very lightly on the forehead, before dragging herself off to her own bedroom.

And lying there, her head throbbing with tension and misery, she was enraged that the persistent picture circling in her head was of Saul and Lowenna chatting solemnly across the breakfast table the morning after her father's funeral, for all the world as if they were an ordinary everyday family. . .a normal father and daughter sitting in the kitchen eating toast together. . .

The telephone seemed to ring non-stop in the morning. First Carol, then Sarah, concerned about Francesca's sudden disappearance from the party. The third call was from Gabriel Andrada, his husky Spanish accent even more pronounced on the other end of the line, inviting her to a special charity exhibition polo match at the Royal Berkshire Club next week. Slightly taken aback by the Argentinian's speed of attack, she hedged. Saul's ice-cold fury last night had triggered her own pride and resentment, but even so the idea of deliberately accepting overtures from his friend Gabriel Andrada made the pit of her stomach sink with a degree of healthy cowardice.

After she had fended off his offers to drive her up there personally, to provide a hotel room funded solely by the match sponsors, no strings, no obligations, he finally gave in and left his telephone number in case she changed her mind. He gave her the number of the Dartview Country Hotel, jolting unwelcome memories as she thoughtfully replaced the receiver. That was the hotel backing on to Hill Mead and Leigh Barton land, the hotel Saul had been staying at for her eighteenth birthday party. . .

His treatment of her then, and his high-handed behaviour last night, made her wish she'd just calmly agreed to Gabriel's suggestions, instead of cautiously refusing.

How dared Saul *tyrannise* her with his threat of marriage? Because that was what it amounted to. The monumental arrogance of it was still smarting inside her head. Did he really think she'd meekly agree to become his wife, when he'd only suggested it out of a misguided sense of duty? Agree to sell Hill Mead to him, just because he wanted it? Arrogant was too mild a word to describe Saul Gallagher—the man was power-crazy.

And what about Charmian? she wondered, with a wry stab of pain. Did Saul have her so well trained she'd just step aside and let him marry another woman? Or maybe she'd just bide her time, and happily resume her relationship with Saul once the knot was tied and the dust had settled. . . After all, Charmian was clearly Saul's type of woman. The four-year silence after their one and only sexual fiasco had proved, resoundingly, that Francesca was *not*.

When the telephone rang again she snatched it up tensely, expecting a call from Saul. But it was Howard Graham, unexpectedly in Devon for the weekend, wondering if she was free for a pub snack that night. Grimly, she agreed to that. In fact, if the entire male membership of the BSJA rang her up and asked her for a date, she'd have booked them ahead for the next few months on consecutive nights. Thanks to Saul she was fighting a losing battle over her reputation locally. And she might have stopped short of flitting off to Berkshire with Gabriel, but if Saul Gallagher was labouring under the misguided impression she was now his personal property, to order around as he chose, she was quite keen to dispel that notion with all suitable speed.

It looked like being a busy week in more ways than one, she reflected bleakly, glancing at the bookings in the diary in the stable office.

She was absorbed in the entertaining procedure of schooling Lowenna and Cobber on a lunge-rope, with Spike comically trotting round and round after them, when Saul clattered into the stable-yard on the huge black gelding he'd taken the night before, its fine dark coat glistening in the morning sun. Gina and Lydia both converged on him from the tack-room, eager to offer assistance.

'Saul!' With the agility of a child twice her age, Lowenna had scrambled down from Cobber's back, abandoning Francesca and running up to Saul as he dismounted. 'Can I ride your horse? What's she called?' Spike had followed, barking delightedly up at Saul, making the big thoroughbred horse snort nervously down its velvety nostrils.

'It's a he. His name's Shadow. You can sit on his back if you like.' Lifting her high in the air, he deposited the beaming child in the saddle, keeping a safe hold on the reins. There was an unmistakable flare of possessiveness in the grey eyes as they scrutinised the little girl fearlessly astride the enormous black horse. It made Francesca's heart contract involuntarily. As she walked slowly over to meet them the warmth and laughter faded abruptly from Saul's expression.

The dark face returned to a blank, unreadable mask as he stared down at her.

'I'd like a brief word in private—can we ride together?' It was more an order than a request, and she stiffened.

'I'm busy this morning—and there's nothing to say!' she said flatly. In brown boots, breeches and battered Barbour, he looked wonderful. Her throat drying, she quickly averted her eyes, trying to keep her emotions under control.

'In that case, I just came to say I'll be away for a few days,' he said in a low, clipped voice. 'I've got some business to attend to. Besides, I don't know about you, but I could do with a cooling-off period. I need to get my thoughts straight. I wasn't being too rational last night—I said some fairly wild things in the heat of the moment!'

The pain which gripped her was out of all proportion to the simple statement. . . What was the matter with her? She'd been dreading Saul marching over here and hurling wedding dates in her face. Now, because he appeared to be having second thoughts, she felt torn apart. There was no logic in it at all.

Shadow was nuzzling Saul's chest, whickering softly, ears pricked forward. Lowenna, full of importance, leaned forward to stroke the rippling muscles of the horse's neck.

'Can I ride with you, Saul?' she pleaded. 'On Cobber?'

'OK. Once round the paddock.' Lowenna was duly transferred to the small dappled pony, and, with Saul remounted on Shadow and holding the leading-rein, the tall man and the diminutive figure of the child receded into the distance, Saul's precise control of the elegant thoroughbred filling Francesca with reluctant admiration all over again. Gabriel was wrong about South Americans having the monopoly on natural horsemanship. Saul Gallagher didn't just ride a horse; man and animal seemed mysteriously integrated, they moved as one. . .

'When will you be back?' she asked with delicate lack of emphasis as he returned a flushed and excited Lowenna safely to the stable-yard.

'Within the next seven days, I imagine.'

'Are you leaving Shadow here again?'

'No, my groom's established at Leigh Barton now. I'll ride back on him.'

Instead of saying goodbye to Francesca, he lifted the child down from Cobber then tossed her lightly up in the air so that she gurgled with delighted laughter, catching her for a brief hug before he stood her back on her feet. 'Goodbye, little one. See you soon.'

'Bye, Saul. . .'

In numb silence, Francesca watched him go. He took the bridleway up towards the birch wood, which bordered her land and his. As he reached the open stretch of meadow, she saw him urge the horse into a canter and then a flat-out gallop, watching until they were just a black speck in the distance. She was glad of the accounts to occupy her mind for the next hour or two, while Ellen took Lowenna into town to buy a birthday present to take to a playgroup friend's party the following week.

She was totting up an endless column of figures on the calculator when Charmian Baron rang.

'I'd like to see you,' the husky voice began, without preamble. Heart suddenly thudding, Francesca frowned at her dim reflection in the mirror on the office wall. 'Are you free tonight, at about eight p.m.?'

'No. Sorry——'

'You're going out?'

'I'm——' To hell with the woman, Francesca thought crossly, what business was it of hers? 'I'm having a drink with a friend.'

'Oh. . .well, maybe I could drop by and see you there? Where are you going?'

'I hardly think——'

'It won't take long!'

She drew in her breath sharply, curiosity suddenly overcoming her resistance. 'Look, I'll be in the Bell having a pub snack between eight and ten,' she spelled out with forced politeness, 'but obviously I won't be alone. If there's something. . .something private you want to discuss, and if it's so urgent, why on earth can't you talk about it now, on the phone?'

'I'm better dealing with things face to face,' Charmian purred smoothly, 'and I'm rather tied up today, packing.'

'I see.' The pain was back, this time a piercing spasm twisting through her stomach. She bit her lip hard to stop herself from saying something extremely rude to the woman on the other end of the phone. 'Should I say I'll look forward to seeing you?' She couldn't erase the dry sarcasm from her voice.

'That rather depends. *Ciao* for now.'

The rest of the day was a grim plod through the everyday routines and chores, but heart leaden, the only aspect keeping her going the natural curiosity aroused by Charmian's mysterious phone call.

* * *

'You're rather quiet tonight, Francesca.' Howard Graham's open, ruddy-faced good humour across the brass-topped table in the Bell Inn was beginning to fade to genuine bewilderment. He scratched his blond head in concern. 'Are you feeling all right?'

'I've got things on my mind. Sorry, Howard. I shouldn't have agreed to come out with you tonight.'

'Don't say that!' he protested, eyeing with approval her slender curves in tight denims and red sweatshirt. 'It's ages since I've seen you. Taking you out for a snack is one of the highlights of my trips to Devon!'

'I enjoyed it, honestly. And I've enjoyed listening to all the latest Show Jumping Association gossip. I appreciate your friendship, Howard.'

Howard went slightly pinker. 'And I jolly well appreciate yours, Francesca. In fact, I was going to ask you——'

'Oh, there you are!'

Whatever it was that Howard was going to ask was lost as Charmian Baron, sleekly beautiful in coffee silk blouse and matching linen trousers, a fine checked wool jacket slung over her shoulders, discreet gold gleaming at ears, throat and wrist, threaded her way to their table.

Howard stood up, pulling out a chair for her. But Charmian stayed on her feet, abruptly waving away his offer of a drink.

'Thank you so much, but please don't bother,' she said, the husky purr more cat-like than ever. 'I'm not staying long.'

There was a short, awkward silence as they all stared at each other uncertainly. Francesca met the deep brown eyes and, in spite of her inkling that Charmian Baron was out to make trouble tonight, felt a jolt of dismay at the expression she read there. The other woman's gaze was hard with dislike and contempt as it swept critically over her make-up-free face and her casual plait.

'Well, you said you wouldn't be here alone, but I must say I hardly expected you to be with a man!'

'What?' With a half-laugh, Francesca kept the lid on her temper, scarcely able to believe her ears. 'Charmian, you said you wanted to see me tonight. Just say what you want to say, would you, please? I've had a long, hard day and I think I'm entitled to enjoy my glass of wine and my bowl of moussaka in peace.'

'I haven't got a lot to say,' Charmian said softly. 'In fact, I really just wanted to satisfy my curiosity! Since I've every reason to consider myself as good as engaged to Saul, I just wanted to take a good, long look at the female Saul Gallagher *claims* he's going to marry!'

She looked down her straight nose at Francesca with a humourless smile. 'Don't hold your breath waiting for him to repeat the offer, will you, darling? You could end up turning a nasty shade of puce! In a few minutes, Saul and I are off to London to spend a few days together and, unless you're very thick-skinned, I think that tells you *all* you need to know.'

CHAPTER EIGHT

FRANCESCA'S friendship with Howard Graham would definitely never be quite the same again, she reflected numbly, going through the motions of hosting a good-bye Sunday lunch for Carol the next day. Charmian's verbal assault last night had cast an embarrassed pall over the remainder of her evening, and she and Howard had parted with awkward formality.

Her life, decided Francesca, was developing a very unpleasant similarity to one of those fairground rides, spinning her backwards and forwards with sickening jolts, making her yearn to jump off and find herself a tranquil hiding-place to recover. With Saul away, and with the need to present a brave face for Lowenna's benefit, her only weapon seemed to be to effect a calm resignation she was far from feeling, and await further developments. But a despairing sense of unreality was enveloping her.

The unnatural calm persisted nearly all day, giving her the composure to question Carol about Charmian Baron as they walked in the bluebell woods after lunch. But Carol appeared to be as ignorant of Saul's plans as she was. Apart from hinting that her son must have a very strong, powerful reason for moving back to Devon, choosing Leigh Barton as his base, and expressing sadness that the university could grant her no further leave to enjoy her newly found great-niece's company, Saul's mother had an air of fence-sitting—all very commendable, Francesca thought frustratedly;

after all, who wanted an interfering relative? But no help at all in easing the anger and confusion whirling round inside her.

She tried not to feel hurt. After all, she understood. Carol's deliberate distance, her calm refusal to be drawn in, stemmed, Francesca felt sure, from her own grim experiences with overbearing in-laws and relatives. Family interference had broken up her relationship with Saul's real father. The gypsy's Gorgio bride had been hounded out of the clan. Yet another family's interference had caused untold problems in her marriage to Harry. . .

Guilty that she couldn't confide in Carol, she was abruptly smitten by doubts and self-recrimination. Carol spoke about Lowenna as her great-niece—what was she going to feel when she discovered Francesca's deception—found out that Lowenna was her grandchild? But to confide in Carol now would seem like putting emotional pressure on Saul. . .she'd look as if she *wanted* to marry him, and she most definitely did not want that. Not in the circumstances. There was no genuine love there—not on Saul's side. Her own feelings were too painful to analyse, but Saul didn't love her; that was obvious. If he'd loved her he'd never have treated her with such cold contempt four years ago, and he'd have stayed. . .he wouldn't have gone off to pursue his exciting career and totally ignored her existence until now.

The bleak, lonely feeling inside when she'd waved Carol off on her journey back to Warwickshire was swallowed up in bitter disappointment the following afternoon. Angus, coming into the stable office waving an innoculation form to be signed, stared in concern at her white, set face.

'Are you OK, Chessy? You look as if you've seen a ghost!'

'I've just heard from Oldfield and Jacks—the estate agents handling the sale of that land—that someone's outbid me. I've lost it.'

'Ah. . .' Angus scratched his sandy beard reflectively. 'The stretch Coombe Farm was selling? I overheard a rumour in the surgery this morning, as a matter of fact. Someone was saying your cousin Saul has bought it.'

'Saul? Are you serious?' She stared at Angus's freckled face disbelievingly. As his words sank in, her stunned dismay rapidly changed to a murderous fury which almost frightened her. '*Saul* has bought that twenty-acre field? You're sure, Angus?'

'Just a rumour, mind. . .' Angus gave a half-grin '. . .but from a fairly reliable source. . .'

And a rumour with a certain grim ring of truth, now she came to think about it, she reflected wrathfully. She clenched her fingers painfully hard on top of the pile of bills and entry forms she'd been dealing with, her mind racing. He'd asked her about it the other day, of course, so casually. . .pumped her about the kind of price she was offering, whether it was going to auction or open to bids; then he'd gone behind her back and bought it himself, no doubt as a means of undermining her expansion plans, thus forcing her to sell out the stables to him. Of all the deceitful, underhand. . .

She felt as if she'd explode with anger.

Blindly grabbing her address book, she began leafing violently through the pages and found the number she wanted. Snatching up the receiver, she began dialling with vengeful precision. Her mind was suddenly made up. If Saul could behave like this. . .if he could buy that land knowing it would ruin her business plans, if he could announce they were getting married when he was already engaged to another woman, if he could virtually *rape* her in the attics at Leigh Barton, for heaven's sake. . . Did Saul really think he could come back to Devon, throw his weight around, take whatever he wanted just because he was now amazingly rich and powerful, order her into some sort of subservient obedience on the strength of having accidentally fathered her child?

She'd go to Berkshire with Gabriel Andrada. Saul could go to hell.

'Are you phoning Saul?' Angus was watching her with a trace of anxiety.

'No. He's away in London,' she said calmly, listening to the ringing tone with the blood pounding in her ears. 'I'm just arranging a day out for myself, at a polo match.'

The Royal Berkshire conveyed an air of well-tended exclusivity, basking in the warm May sunshine. Sun glinted off manicured emerald lawns and snowy-white paling fences, gilded the neat black and white clock-tower above the handsome red-brick Victorian stable-blocks. A huge marquee tent rustled blue and white in a light breeze, real champagne was being drunk from real champagne glasses, Raybans and colourful designer outfits were jostling for position, while BMWs and Aston Martins and personal helicopters whirred to and fro at the edge of the field.

It was all quite delightful, and Francesca wished she could honestly say she was enjoying herself.

'You look fantastic!' Sarah had enthused, inspecting the effect of the hyacinth-blue and white spotted dress she'd helped to choose for the occasion. The tight bodice had a low cross-over neckline, the skirt was knee-length and slightly gathered, revealing a long expanse of well-shaped leg, and a short-sleeved shoulder-padded jacket in plain blue went with it. Shiny round blue earrings and a matching bead necklace matched clutch-bag and low-heeled pumps to perfection. It was dressy, summery, and had made rather a hole in Francesca's normally thrift-conscious savings. But the devil-may-care fury triggered by the phone call from Oldfield and Jacks had made her splash out for once.

'With your skin and eyes the effect is stunning, Chessy!' Sarah had hesitated a fraction of a second before adding casually, 'Will Saul be there too?'

The question was revolving in her head now like a record stuck in a groove. The answer, she suspected, was 'of course'. She hadn't asked Gabriel outright, and he hadn't mentioned Saul at all on their drive up the motorway. But she somehow knew he'd be here. He'd be playing. And wasn't that the only reason she'd agreed to come here with Gabriel Andrada today? The guilty truth was niggling around at the back of her mind, waiting to trap her into silent confession.

'Have some more champagne, Francesca.' Gabriel picked up the bottle from the round white table on the bar terrace, dark eyes gleaming appreciatively over her glossy French plait, the golden curve of her breasts just visible at the low neck of her dress, her figure slender beneath the slim-fitting outfit. 'We must celebrate!'

'Celebrate?' She smiled politely, raising enquiring eyebrows. 'Celebrate what? With a slight jolt of panic, she realised she knew nothing at all about this man. Nothing personal, that was. Nothing that could possibly put them on a truly *friendly* footing. He was a polo acquaintance of Saul's, of course. That was either a recommendation or a condemnation, depending which way you looked at it. Gabriel's stay in the West Country had been connected with a horse he was thinking of buying. That was the extent of her knowledge. And their conversation since he'd picked her up from Hill Mead very early that morning had been general and impersonal, mainly consisting of a monologue on the problems of choosing the right kind of horse since, in addition to attending horse sales in Devon, Gabriel was apparently in the habit of scouring the wilds of New Zealand, Australia, Mexico and Brazil as well as Argentina to pin down that elusive breed of polo pony he required. The best, he assured her proudly, were criollos, Argentinian working cattle ponies descended from the Andalusian war horses of the conquistadors.

Even with her own natural interest in horses of all shapes and sizes, she'd guiltily felt her eyes glazing. She'd tactfully refrained from asking why he bothered to travel the world so extensively with such national treasures on his own doorstep.

Having exhausted the subject of horses, he'd gone into minute detail about the crushed bones and mutilated limbs he'd personally witnessed in savage polo matches out in South America, until Francesca's stomach turned in disgust.

Now here she was, all dressed up, sipping champagne, out for the day with a perfect stranger. In the black fury with Saul she'd even blithely trusted Gabriel's generous promise to arrange tonight's hotel accommodation before she caught a train back to Devon tomorrow.

'What are we celebrating?' she asked lightly. 'It's not your birthday, is it, Gabriel?'

The Argentinian tossed his dark head back and laughed. 'No, it is not my birthday. And perhaps it is not for you to celebrate, but only for me!'

'I still don't follow.'

'I celebrate scoring a small victory over my very good friend, Saul Gallagher!' Gabriel grinned, watching her expression with a slightly sheepish air. Francesca stared at him, then smiled back faintly, her cheeks reddening.

'You are blushing. Enchanting!' Gabriel laughed again, his smile fading. '*You* are enchanting, *cara*! I am greatly honoured that you are here with me!'

'Gabriel—what you said about scoring victories?' She took a quick sip of champagne, looking him squarely in the eye. 'I'm afraid I may be guilty of the same motive in coming here with you today.'

'Ah, yes.' There was a certain rueful charm about Gabriel Andrada, she decided, watching his slow nod of understanding and silently praying for his forebearance.

'I mean. . .it's not that I didn't want to come as your guest today, but—but I. . .' she began to add hurriedly, feeling terrible. Gabriel put his arm around her shoulders, and kissed her cheek.

'Do not look so worried, *cara*. I think maybe Gabriel Andrada's ego is big enough to cope with this situation.' Sliding his finger round to tilt up her chin, he added softly, 'But I hope, too, that you find me just a little bit attractive. Just as I find you very, very attractive, Francesca. . .'

Before she could retract her head, he'd kissed her full on the mouth, and she'd just had time to register no sensation whatsoever when an angry exclamation behind her made her jump violently.

'What the hell's going on?' Saul demanded with soft menace in his voice. Gabriel released her, his eyes quizzical as he noted Saul's venomous expression. Francesca took a rebellious sip of her champagne, wishing her fingers would stop shaking. In full polo gear, red shirt with a white number four on the sleeves, red and white sash bearing the legend 'Baron' across his chest, white breeches and long brown leather boots, he looked so diabolically attractive that her throat dried as she stared at him. 'Francesca, what in the devil's name are you doing?' Saul was flexing his fingers as he buttoned on his soft leather gloves, his actions aggressively jerky.

'I'm drinking champagne, and kissing Gabriel.' She smiled sweetly, belatedly realising that this was her third glass and that high-quality Bollinger packed a fearful punch. 'How about you? Where's the delectable Charmian?'

The grey eyes scythed into her so ferociously that she almost took a step back, but stood her ground just in time to salvage her composure.

'If this weren't a *charity* match,' he grated venomously, taking in her appearance in one sweeping, bitter glance, 'I'd sort this out right now. 'But at least I'll have the satisfaction of playing *against* you, Andrada.'

'Have you and Charmian named the great day yet?' Francesca enquired with breezy coolness.

'What the hell are you talking about?'

'I'm talking about your engagement to Charmian Baron. Funnily enough, I thought her name was familiar when I first met her. Her father owns Baron Wines, doesn't he? He sponsors some of the polo teams you play for. Really, Saul, you must be losing your touch in your quest for fame and fortune— Charmian's a far better catch than I am!'

'Are you drunk?'

'Not in the least.' She suppressed the tiniest hiccup and managed a mocking smile. 'That's not a very gentlemanly thing to say, Saul!'

'I've never claimed to be a gentleman.'

There was a jovial male voice on the PA system announcing the imminent start of the match. Out of the corner of her eye, she noticed Charmian in a sun-reflecting black and white suit, blonde hair piled high, chatting with a group of VIPs at the marquee entrance. The hard brown eyes flashed more than once in Francesca's direction. She was beginning to feel under fire from every angle. Not for the first time she regretted the furious impulse to come here with Gabriel.

'Cool down, *amigo*,' Gabriel began, reaching out to pat Saul's shoulder and receiving a glare almost fierce enough to ignite a nearby tree. 'I have been taking very great care of your cousin. Francesca is quite safe with me——'

'If anyone concerns themselves with Francesca's safety, *amigo*, it will be me,' Saul drawled icily, turning abruptly on his heel to march over to the lines where a groom was in charge of Saul's string of horses, expertly tacking up a magnificent chestnut mare, a blue and white striped *mandille* under the saddle, yellow band-aged legs, plaited mane and tail bound with matching tape. With effortless ease he swung into the saddle and leaned his stick over his shoulder, glancing down at her as he rode back down along the edge of the field. 'I'll see you after the match, Francesca.'

A veiled threat was somehow implicit in the words. Unsure whether to laugh, cry or shout abuse, she lifted her hand in a light, mutinous wave as he joined the rest of the players, and the eight riders thundered into action.

The match seemed to stretch on endlessly. She should be enjoying it, she thought; relaxing, absorbing the excitement and the tension, losing herself like the rest of the crowd in the creak of boots on leathers, the clatter of bamboo on bamboo, the dust and the shouts and Cossack-style grace as sticks were swung and the white ball flew around the field. . . The trouble was she was simmering with indignation. Saul had somehow managed to leave her feeling like a disobedient school-girl standing outside the headmaster's office, waiting for suitable chastisement. It took all her pride and determination to hold her own fierce anger up as a shield, to keep herself from quietly disappearing to the nearest railway station and hopping on a train back to Exeter.

Any hope she had of distracting her thoughts from endlessly circling around the subject of Saul Gallagher were pointless, she realised wryly, since the commentator seemed to refer to him with monotonous regularity, praising his skill, extolling the virtues of his exceptionally aggressive style. . .

'You *do* get around, darling!' Charmian Baron smiled unpleasantly, briefly passing her during the obligatory tread-in between chukkas. 'I'm so pleased to see you're widening your sights a little!'

To her chagrin, Francesca failed to think of a suitably restrained counter-attack. But she was blowed if she'd sink to the level of public slanging matches with Saul's bitchy women friends, she told herself, regaining her seat and watching Saul's team annihilate Gabriel's in a runaway victory which had the commentator in ecstasies as the sweat-stained players finally cantered off the field.

'Well played, my friend,' Gabriel said good-naturedly, approaching Francesca at Saul's side, 'even if you did nearly kill me in that last ride off.'

'I can't deny the temptation,' Saul told him brusquely, his eyes on Francesca. 'Sorry to spoil your plans for aprés-polo partying, but you and I have some serious talking to do.'

'Can't it wait?'

'No. It can't wait.'

Saul had taken her arm, and Gabriel, catching the outraged expression on her face, took a step forward, his dark skin flushing slightly.

'Hey. . .the lady came with me,' he began warningly, real temper flaring in his dark eyes.

'And she's leaving now, with me.' The pale, brutal glitter of Saul's glare was almost blinding in its intensity, far more chilling and threatening than the straightforward pique in the other man's expression. Towering head and shoulders taller than Gabriel, Saul looked an awesome adversary.

Momentarily, the three stood locked in silent, furious conflict. Francesca felt angrily helpless. Saul's fingers were biting into her arm. Nothing she could say could defuse the situation, but her temper was rapidly reaching boiling point. Saul was behaving like a loathsome, barbarous thug. If she appealed to Gabriel to side with her she'd be goading them to further hostilities—she had a sudden shameful vision of the two men fighting over her, right here in the sophisticated surroundings of the polo club. . .

'It's all right, Gabriel,' she managed to say with calm irony, 'Saul and I do have some *differences* to sort out——'

'Then maybe you two should sort out your differences in private!' the Argentinian suggested shortly, flicking a finger lightly under Francesca's chin before stalking off towards the bar, his stiff bearing conveying the depth of his displeasure as he half turned back towards Saul. 'But if your cousin wishes to spend time with me in the future, *amigo*, I will not be so accommodating!'

'Saul, that was *unforgivable!*' she hissed fiercely, but he was already frogmarching her to his car, hurling sticks and hard hat into the rear of the Range Rover, peeling off his gloves and pushing her into the passenger seat with almost the same cavalier roughness. She glared across at him, her blue eyes deep purple with fury. His dark hair was plastered to his head from the sweat of the match; perspiration beaded his forehead. Even hot and dishevelled and sweaty after the game, his shirt sticking to his chest, white breeches dust-stained, his sensual aura was powerful and undeniable. This knowledge fuelled her outrage, set her pulses hammering. 'How *could* you behave like that?'

'Upset Gabriel, you mean?' The powerful engine roared into life, and they were swinging out of the grounds on to the open road, leaving behind the exotic rarity of the club for the real world, the atmosphere crackling with tension. 'I've only wounded his inflated Latin ego. He'll survive.'

'This. . .this Neanderthal man behaviour is an aspect of your character I hadn't noticed in the past,' she went on witheringly. 'I suppose I should have known what to expect after the way you hauled me out of your housewarming party for daring to hold a conversation with a fellow guest!'

'Francesca. . .' Saul suddenly swore uncouthly under his breath, spinning the wheel so that they hurtled off the main road on to a small country lane, accelerating along between high shady oaks and beech trees and finally braking hard by a gateway to a wide, rippling green wheatfield. Pulling into the entrance, he cut the engine and ran his hand across his face in a gesture of exhaustion. 'This is crazy—why are we arguing about Gabriel Andrada, for the love of heaven?'

'Don't ask me! Maybe we should be arguing about Charmian Baron, or your unscrupulous deceit over that land I wanted.'

'The *land*? Oh, hell, I can explain about the land.'

'I'm sure. Let's hear it—let me guess: it's a free world, a free market, bids were invited and you had just as much right to put in an offer as I did?' She was trembling slightly with tension and reaction to the ugly scene at the club, and her passionate resentment of his overbearing interference.

Saul was searching impatiently in the glove compartment, extracting a battered packet of thin black cheroots. Thrusting one in his mouth with barely suppressed violence, he lit it and surveyed her through a cloud of aromatic smoke.

'I didn't know you smoked——'

'I've given up.'

'Evidently.' She was delicately sarcastic, but he ignored the taunt.

'That land. . . You may not believe this, but I put my bid in as insurance,' he said curtly, kicking open the door and climbing out of the car to lean on the doorframe. 'Dartview Country Club were after it—I had a tip-off from a friend of mine that they were offering a lot of money, planning to extend facilities— you'd have missed out on it anyway——'

'Then why didn't you say something?' she demanded hotly, getting out too and marching to the front of the Range Rover, feeling the young wheat stalks scratching her legs. 'I could have offered more——'

'Could you?' The glance she received was derisive. 'I've tried to hold several reasonable conversations with you since I came back to Devon, Francesca. Each time you've slammed a verbal door in my face. I said nothing about the land because I didn't think for one second you'd listen to me. You haven't exactly been clamouring for my help and advice!'

She faced him, her smile scathing. 'So you just bought the land for yourself? *Very* helpful.'

'I bought the land,' Saul explained in ominous patience, 'to prevent an expanding country club owning the stretch between Hill Mead and Leigh Barton. My intention was to let you use it as you wished, or——'

'I'm not a charity case!' she exploded.

'—or, if you prefer, rent it from me,' Saul finished up shortly, his face a stiff mask of anger. 'I was trying to help someone who's so goddamned prickly she's almost impossible to help! But frankly the land is a red herring, Francesca. I couldn't give a damn about it. What worries me is how you can go out to pubs with other men——'

'Oh, Charmian told you she'd seen me, did she?'

'—and encourage the attentions of a practised Lothario like Gabriel Andrada, let him maul you and kiss you right in front of me, then niggle at this trivia over the land when the question of *our* daughter's future needs to be resolved!'

She stared at him in silence, her heart thudding. 'That's not fair, Saul!' she whispered hoarsely. 'How can you even *suggest* that Lowenna's future isn't important to me?'

'Because of the way you behave?' he suggested caustically. 'If that child's future is important to you, why the *hell* didn't you give me the chance to give her a normal start in life?'

'She's had a normal start in life, all the love, all the security *any* child could want!'

'Except for a father!'

'What was I supposed to do? Run after you, follow you halfway round the world, just on the off-chance you might consent to becoming a family man?' she grated bitterly, her voice choking in her throat. 'Knowing the way you'd accused me of throwing myself at half the population of Bellbridge before I finally ended up in bed with you?'

Tears were hot behind her eyelids, but pride and anger held them back.

Saul flinched slightly. 'You should have told me,' he repeated, his voice low. 'And I can't help feeling the reason you didn't was because your father loathed me.'

'No! You're wrong, Saul! I didn't tell you because you didn't love me, and no relationship can survive without love——'

'Francesca. . .'

'Not only that, you seemed to despise me!' Her chin shot up at the darkening expression on his face, her fierce restraint disintegrating as the memories flooded back. 'I was so *glad* to see you at my birthday party, Saul! I'd missed you so much! I'll admit it to you! I'll tell you the truth about how I felt, because nothing you can do now can hurt me that much again, Saul!'

'Chessy. . .' There was a husky sternness in the interruption, but she ignored him, some inner compulsion bringing the words tumbling out unchecked.

'I'd always loved you! But when I saw you that night it was different. . .it felt a different kind of love! I didn't just love you like a brother or a cousin. When you made love to me the next day, it felt so right. . .and it was the first time any man had made me feel that way.' It was a bitter torrent, finally finding an outlet.

Saul's dark face had flushed slightly. He'd gone deadly still, his eyes probing hers with an intensity which made her tremble inwardly.

When he finally spoke his voice had altered, roughened slightly. 'Can I enquire whether those feelings have totally disappeared, Chessy?'

'You mean, do I still love you?' she managed to whisper raggedly. 'Give me credit for some sense, Saul! I'm not a total masochist! After those things you said to me—even if you hadn't spent the intervening years as far away from me as you could possibly get without catching a rocket to the moon—there's a limit to the amount of pain anyone can endure! Even love's not indestructible!'

'Isn't it?' The rejoinder had a caustic bitterness to it. Saul threw down the cheroot in disgust and ground it hard into the soil with his heel before crossing the distance between them and taking hold of her arms. 'Maybe that depends on the kind of love we're talking about. Are we discussing *wanting* someone—adolescent sexual fantasies—or the sort of love you talked about the other night, when I asked you to marry me?'

'What are you talking about?'

'Chessy. . .those ground-rules for a happy marriage

you listed—the mutual understanding, the support, the sharing? Do you imagine I don't want them as well?'

'You're not capable of giving them!'

'Are *you*? You sure as hell weren't four years ago! Don't you have any *idea* how much I wanted to be with you then?' He gave her a slight, rough shake, and she stared at him blankly.

'You're not making any sense!'

'Francesca, when I said we had to do some talking, I had a feeling it was going to prove an uphill struggle, but——'

The shrilling of his car-phone interrupted the soft, intense speech. With a muttered oath he swung away and reached to answer it. Suddenly exhausted, Francesca leaned weakly against the warm bodywork of the Range Rover, her eyes unfocused on the distant shimmer of heat on the green horizon. Saul's words had stirred up a hornet's nest of emotions inside her. She wished she could clear her brain, think straight. But the tension, the champagne, the anger at being dragged from the polo club like a naughty child—it had all conspired to fill her head with cotton wool.

Then something in Saul's voice brought her rigidly upright, every tiny nerve-end alive.

'. . .just calm down—which hospital?' he was saying in an urgent, soothing kind of tone which she'd heard him use on frightened horses and aggressive dogs with devastating success. '. . . Devon and Exeter. And she's all right?'

'Saul! What is it? Who is it?'

'Ellen. Lowenna's been involved in an accident——'

'Is she all right? What sort of accident?' A whirl of bleak panic was engulfing her. Eyes staring out of her head, she grabbed Saul's arm, shaking him slightly. 'Saul? Is she all right?'

'As far as I can make out,' he said curtly as she swept the phone from his hand and began to question Ellen with as much calm as she could muster, while her heart felt as if it would burst inside her ribs and her throat dried to sandpaper. Immediately, the reason for Saul's cryptic answer became clear. Ellen was crying so hard it was difficult to get a coherent sentence out of her.

Handing the phone back to Saul, Francesca stared at him in acute distress.

'She's had another bash at riding Vengeance, from what I can gather. He promptly bolted with her and bucked her off into a thick thorn hedge. She's alive, but whether it's bumps and bruises or a broken leg or worse, I can't make out! Saul, I have to get home, *now*. . .' Ellen's hysteria was catching, Francesca realised dimly. A slight rise in pitch at the end of her sentence made her pull herself up short.

Saul was glancing at his watch, eyes bleak. The only sign of emotion was a muscle working spasmodically in his cheek.

'We'll go back to the club and take Jim Roberts's Sikorsky. . .'

'What?'

'It's four hours in the car, one hour by helicopter.'

Within minutes they were speeding back to the club, rapid telephone calls clinching the loan of Jim Roberts's Sikorsky complete with pilot and even a taxi to meet them at the heliport at the other end. It was all accomplished so fast that within twenty minutes Francesca found herself strapped into the passenger seat of one of the most expensive privately owned helicopters in the world, earphones and mouthpiece clipped to her head, Saul beside her, an obliging pilot at the controls. The whole thing had such an 'other-worldly' air about it, like an unreal scene from an up-market television thriller, that she had to dig her nails into her palms to convince herself it was really happening.

But the sick anxiety in the pit of her stomach was real. The anguish she was clamping quietly inside her was only too real. She felt *crushed* by guilt. There she was, all dressed up, enjoying a luxury day out, drinking champagne and eating smoked salmon and caviare, while her little three-year-old daughter managed to evade supervision long enough to be involved in a potentially fatal accident. . . The list of recriminations, 'if onlys', and self-doubts was growing longer and longer.

With a silent groan, she shut her eyes tightly, but all she could see in her mind's eye, as they followed the distant snakes of motorways and 'A' roads below, buzzing police cars at a hundred and thirty miles per hour without fear of prosecution, was a gruesome vision of Lowenna—hurt, confused, frightened, maybe surrounded by strangers, needing her to be there, with her, to make everything all right again.

Abruptly it seemed as if her whole perspective had shifted. The hostility with Saul, her fury over his arrogant interference—all of it seemed to blur into insignificance. The only truly important thing was to find Lowenna safe and sound when they got back to Devon.

When Saul reached a lean brown hand across and took her cold fingers in his, she didn't pull away.

CHAPTER NINE

'SHE's a bit shaken up, but she's fine. We'll keep her in for the night, though, to be on the safe side.' The sister's smile was calmly encouraging, as Francesca sat on the edge of the high hospital bed, gazing with suspiciously bright eyes at the small irrepressibly cheerful face against the pillows. The relief after the fraught, nightmare journey back was so intense that she felt almost light-headed with happiness.

The only signs of Lowenna's recent ordeal were a worrying absence of colour in her cheeks, and a great deal of sticking-plaster.

'Wenna, darling, promise Mummy you won't do anything like that again?' Francesca said quietly, holding a small hand between both of hers and rejoicing in the blissful reassurance that her daughter was relatively unharmed.

'No. . .all right. . .' The child's face furrowed thoughtfully. 'But I wanted to make Vengeance go as fast as you and Saul can. . .and he looked lonely. . .'

'And Cobber will be even lonelier while he's waiting for you to come home from hospital!'

'It's a good thing three-year-olds bounce so well,' Saul added calmly, earning himself a couple of points in Francesca's eyes by resisting the temptation to launch into a lecture on safety.

'We thought at first there could be a greenstick fracture of the collarbone,' the nurse added, 'but the doctor thinks it's only bruises and scratches. The overnight stay is really only a precaution.'

'Can I stay with her?'

'Of course, althought there's really no need. It's not as if she's in for an operation or anything.'

'But I'd feel happier being here,' Francesca insisted quietly, 'if it's no trouble.'

'No trouble at all, Mrs St Aubyn——'

'It's *Miss* St Aubyn.'

'Oh. Fine.' The sister glanced swiftly from Francesca to Saul with a brisk professional smile. 'But it's late already and Lowenna will be quite safe with us.

The slight accent on 'safe' might have been a product of Francesca's guilty imagination. But she coloured slightly, catching Saul's eyes.

'I'll tell you what we'll do, Lowenna,' he suggested calmly, coming round the bed to put his arm lightly across Francesca's shoulders and ignoring the sudden stiffening in her body, 'I'll take Mummy home with me while I get changed, then I'll take her out for a meal, and I'll bring her back in the morning to see you. OK?'

The child nodded enthusiastically.

'It's OK, Mummy. I'm a big girl now. I'm going to watch television and have a bedtime drink and a biscuit. I don't mind staying here on my own! The food's lovely. I had fish-fingers and tomato ketchup and alphabet spaghetti for my tea. And ice-cream and chocolate sauce.'

'Sounds delicious,' Saul agreed solemnly. 'Mummy might like something slightly different, though.'

The decision seemed to have been made for her. Quelling an odd twist of pain that her infant daughter appeared so calmly independent, she gave Lowenna a fierce hug and a goodnight kiss, with promises to see her first thing in the morning. The look Saul gave her over Lowenna's head as he reached to ruffle the tousled dark hair on the pillow felt almost like a direct shot of adrenalin, it was so unguardedly brilliant and full of emotion.

Francesca felt suddenly all at sea. The angry armour she'd been using for protection felt as if it was remorselessly cracking apart.

'Well?' he queried softly, as the taxi dropped them off at Hill Mead. 'Where would you like to go, Chessy?'

'I'm exhausted, Saul. I'm really not very hungry, are you?'

'I'm ravenous.' He looked at her through narrowed eyes, and her stomach did another involuntary jump. 'And we have to talk, Francesca.'

She stared at him numbly, seeing the justice of this. It was true; they did have to talk. If only to agree with painful frankness on the lack of future between them.

'Yes,' she said miserably, avoiding that probing gaze, 'I suppose we do.'

'Say whatever you need to say to Ellen,' Saul recommended quietly, 'then we'll go back to Leigh Barton for a drink while I shower and change. If we can use your Land Rover I'll try and be decisive about where to go and eat. . .though goodness knows, seeing Lowenna in hospital has left me feeling pole-axed.'

With a quick, startled glance at him, she nodded. 'That's how I feel. The thoughts going through my head on the way back from Berkshire belong to the realm of nightmares.'

'But she's all right,' he reminded her with a sudden gentleness which shook her composure to the core, 'and she's a terrific, spirited little girl, Chessy. She's fearless and independent, and quite frankly, apart from your unfortunate choice of nannies, I don't think I could fault her upbringing in any way!'

'I'll take that as a compliment, even if it's not,' she returned quietly, a lump forming in her throat, gazing at Saul gravely before going slowly inside for the inevitable debriefing with Ellen, who was drinking tea in the kitchen with Mrs Prince and Gina, still tearful and remorseful.

Saul was leaning against the Land Rover in the evening sunshine when she emerged, shaken, a few minutes later.

'She's just resigned,' she told him miserably, 'but I feel awful letting her go thinking she'd let me down like that!'

With an encompassing glance at her shattered face he took the keys from her without argument, and she climbed wordlessly into the passenger seat. They drove the short distance to Leigh Barton in silence, Saul sweeping to a halt on the gravel outside the thatched farmhouse and helping her down from the car.

'You're right to let her go. One of the prerequisites of a good nanny is someone who knows where her three-year-old charge is, and what she's up to! Frankly she's no bloody good at her job!' was Saul's blunt opinion. He steered her firmly into the sitting-room and on to one of the sofas, warmed by a pool of sun flooding in through the deep, south-facing windows.

Mrs Venn had laid a fire in the huge inglenook fireplace in case the evening turned chilly, and Saul put a match to this before pouring them both a stiff brandy, downing his with disreputable speed and disappearing upstairs to shower and change out of his sweat-stained polo gear.

Suddeny overcome by tiredness, Francesca was in no

mood to argue with Saul's verdict on Ellen. He was right anyway, she thought wearily. She'd never be able to trust her completely again. But now she'd have to start advertising again, and that was infuriatingly time-consuming *and* it was upsetting for Lowenna.

She gazed around her, her eyes moving slowly from the elegant peach and blue peacock pattern on sofas and curtains, the rich deep shine on the parquet floor reflecting the leaping flames from the fire. A delicate smell of apple logs wafted from the fireplace. The room was beautifully furnished, with mellow old-pine corner cupboards and tables, Windsor chairs either side of the fire and a muted Indian rug which blended with the general colour scheme. A satinwood mantel clock ticked solemnly on the blackened beam of the chimney-piece, flanked by a rosewood and mother-of-pearl barometer, and a row of painted Chelsea plates. Every-where there were sepia prints, or oil-paintings of local Devon scenes. . .it all screamed impeccable taste and loads of money, she reflected, recalling Charmian Baron's role in the redecoration scheme with a bitter stab of jealousy which rocked her with its intensity.

She closed her eyes, drank some more brandy, and tried not to think at all. When Saul reappeared a short while later, his dark hair wet and plastered back, his five o'clock shadow freshly shaved to a respectable smoothness, smelling faintly of some clean, tangy soap or aftershave, she was almost asleep.

'I honestly don't think I'm up to going out to a restaurant,' she said stiffly, as he came to squat down on his haunches in front of her. A shiver of apprehension ran down her spine at his nearness. In soft grey cords and black silk polo shirt, he had such a dramatic effect on her nervous system that she felt her toes curling. The thought of him with Charmian Baron hurt like an abrupt physical stab of pain.

'Mrs Venn said she'd leave something in the fridge for tonight,' Saul said firmly. 'We'll eat here.'

'Saul, I'm grateful for your help today.' She glanced round for the remains of her brandy, sipped the fiery liquid and felt it burn a path downwards, reviving her slightly, bolstering her flagging resolve. 'If it hadn't been for you I'd probably still be driving down the motorway. . .but there's really no need for you to provide food and entertainment.' She took a deep breath, forcing herself to go on. 'I've been thinking, just sitting here. The fright I had today seems to have concentrated my mind quite clearly. You can see as much of Lowenna as you like, Saul, but. . .just don't keep up this pretence of wanting to marry me—surely you can see it wouldn't work? Quite apart from any-thing else, you've been living with Charmian Baron. She's quite entitled to assume you'll be marrying *her*! It's humiliating, feeling as if you're trying to do the honourable thing.'

'So you're suggesting we lead separate lives? With Lowenna the only common denominator?' His expression had darkened, a bitter irony in his voice.

'Yes, if you like.' She swallowed miserably, part of her curling up and dying inside. 'I can see that you're angry over Lowenna; looking at it all from your point of view, I suppose you've a right to be. But you must see it could never have worked out, Saul——'

'OK, that's enough.' He'd stood up, suddenly remote and distant, his eyes unreadable. 'You've had your say for the moment. Just stay there—I'll be back in a minute.'

Saul returned a few seconds later, a determined

gleam in his eyes. 'I'm going to cook us some steaks. . .
How do you like yours?'

'Rare, but Saul I'm really not——'

'I've unearthed a green salad and a French stick in
the larder. And there's fresh raspberries or coffee
gâteau to follow. Would you like another drink while
you're waiting?'

'I. . .' Overwhelmed by his air of cool decisiveness,
she blinked at her half-empty glass. Saul took it from
her numb fingers with a trace of grim amusement,
adding another measure of brandy. 'It's not really an
aperitif, but it should help you relax,' he said calmly,
disappearing into the kitchen and leaving her staring at
the glow of the fire with a sense of being steam-rollered
into submission.

Within an impressive twenty minutes she was seated
opposite Saul at an oval gatelegged table in front of the
fire, exquisitely tender fillet steaks, salad, bread and
wine arranged between them.

'All right. . .' she put down her knife and fork after
a while, watching Saul attack his steak with relish, a
reluctant half-smile curving her lips '. . .I'll admit it—
this is absolutely delicious.'

'Grilling steaks is the extent of my culinary skill, I'm
afraid.'

'You're a brilliant steak chef, Saul. If you're trying
to impress me, you've succeeded. And you've caught
me at a weak moment tonight. Lowenna's near-miss
was nerve-shredding, to say the least.' She took a sip
of the full-bodied Burgundy, and eyed him warily. 'But
I'm painfully aware that supping with the devil might
be more advisable! I warn you I'm not selling Hill
Mead to you, Saul, and as for that land you've managed
to buy, I'm not——'

'Chessy. . .' Saul laid down his knife and fork too, his eyes very bright and hard as he stared at her across the table '. . .can we forget Hill Mead, forget the land? The only matters of any importance are you, and our child.'

The glittering grey gaze was turning her bones to water, but she lifted her chin in cool disbelief, anger kindling in the dark blue of her eyes.

'Don't you agree?' he persisted softly.

Abruptly she looked away from the challenging stare, fighting for composure, concentrating with fierce attention on the contents of her wine glass. There were tiny pinpoints of firelight shimmering ruby flames through the liquid.

'But you've every right to question my motives for asking you to marry me, Francesca.'

'Well, at least we agree on something!'

Saul's face looked paler, his face set grimly. 'Chessy, how can I make you understand? Four years ago. . .four years ago we were both struggling to make sense of our lives. . .in different ways we were both having problems sorting fantasy from reality——'

'Not *that* again!' A flame lit in her eyes. 'I'm sick of being accused of living in a fantasy world, Saul! What I felt for you was *real*—I don't care if you thought it was some fevered fantasy drummed up by my research into the Romany culture! How do you think I felt when I. . .when we'd just made love, to be mocked for harbouring some sick sexual fantasy about macho gypsy lovers chopping off their wives' ears for being unfaithful, or. . .or. . .stripping them and publicly whipping them?'

'That wasn't necessarily what I was referring to,' Saul interposed, his voice husky.

'Well, it's the most vivid memory I have!' she flashed back. 'The most hurtful memory. You. . .you debased something beautiful! You deliberately tried to hurt me. . .'

Saul drew a deep, shaky breath, and fixed her with a haunted, hunted look. 'No. I never meant to hurt you. . .it was myself I was angry with. I love you, Chessy. I loved you then, and I love you now. I think I always have.'

Francesca swallowed hard, staring at him helplessly, suddenly aware of him in every atom of her being. Without warning it seemed as if her world had turned upside-down. She could hardly believe she was sitting here with Saul, in Leigh Barton, hearing him say the simple words she'd once have crossed continents to hear him say. She gazed at him numbly, eyes wide and blank with confusion.

'Oh, hell. . . Francesca. . .' Saul grated his chair back from the table abruptly, rubbing his forehead with a jerky movement. 'I had a complete speech worked out. But, seeing you sitting there. . .my mind's gone blank. . .' His wide mouth twisted in sudden, bleak self-torture. 'Just say you'll marry me? Put me out of my misery?' The latter was a soft anguished drawl, half mocking, but totally failing to disguise his acute tension. It was filling the room, reaching her in tightly coiled tendrils, winding her up inside until she felt like crying.

Instead, she realised, she was shaking her head slowly, a frozen feeling creeping through her. Dimly, miserably, she was aware that Saul was spinning her a ruthlessly clever line. He must honestly think she was a simpleton if he expected her to believe this, fall for this full-frontal assault on her emotions after all that had happened between them. . .

'Saul. . . I'm sorry. . . I don't know what to say. . .' She was vaguely aware of slight incoherence, and started again. 'You say you love me. You say you want to marry me. But none of this makes any sense! If you loved me, why did you treat me the way you did? We—we made love, and then you yelled abuse at me and I didn't see you again for four years! You have to admit it's a strange way of showing you love someone.'

'I'd like to try to explain——'

'I'll bet!' There was anger now, a painful indignation at his assumption of her level of intelligence. 'You'll understand, though, if I'm feeling slightly sceptical? I mean if there's a good, logical reason why you pop up in Bellbridge after all this time, why you try to buy Hill Mead behind my back, why you trick me into confiding in you and then buy the twenty-acre field I need, why you have a glamorous live-in girlfriend in tow who's given the task of doing up your new house for you. . .' She was shaking all over as she finished up coldly, 'Frankly, Saul, the whole thing. . .*stinks*!'

There was a thunderous silence.

'Not a very elegant turn of phrase,' Saul said at length, his lidded expression hiding the brilliance of his eyes. 'But you're right, in a way. The whole thing does stink.'

'Honesty at last.' Somewhere deep inside her heart was breaking all over again, an experience she'd thought could only be endured once.

'Are you prepared to at least hear me out, Francesca?'

'As long as it gets *less* farcicial and improbable, why

not?' She shrugged, her smile brittle, viciously suppressing the urge to howl like a baby.

He stared at her, his eyes sombre. 'I'm not sure where to start. . .'

'How about a brief resumé of your last four years?' she suggested helpfully, sweetly sarcastic. 'Are you going to tell me you've been pining for me all this time? That you haven't enjoyed a single minute of your brilliant polo career?'

'No. . .' Saul was making a conscious effort to control his temper in the face of her scathing onslaught. 'These last four years have been. . .cathartic. My success in polo has given me. . .a sense of identity. On a petty level I suppose it's been satisfying gaining respect from all those contemporaries at Eton who taunted me about my background. Polo was their game. Gaining high-goal professional status was. . .a kind of defiant gesture.'

The hard mouth twisted in self-derision, and she stared at him, fighting down the sympathy.

'You were unhappy at school?'

'Desperately.' Saul grinned suddenly, without much humour, his teeth startlingly white against his skin.

'Why didn't you say something? I can't believe Uncle Harry and Aunt Carol would have made you stay there——'

'I was too proud,' he said flatly. 'If you want a full account of my faults, Francesca, pride and jealousy are top of the list.'

'So if polo was so therapeutic, what suddenly made you change course? Come back here like this?'

'It's quite simple. I heard your father was ill. I heard you were not married, still living at Hill Mead. And I heard Leigh Barton was up for sale.'

She toyed with her fork, trying to piece together the logic. 'You didn't hear about Lowenna?' she queried warily, not meeting his eyes. The probing intensity there was too overwhelming for her fragile composure.

'No. I didn't know about Lowenna until she came trotting into the study that afternoon. I was just about to try and explain my feelings for you when she appeared. Do you know what I thought then? The first moment I saw her?' There was a muscle working in Saul's jaw, the only outward sign of tension. Francesca nevertheless felt herself go very still.

'What did you think?' It was a whisper. Cross with herself, she cleared her throat and picked up her glass to drink some wine.

'For a wild second, I thought "she's mine". Then I realised I was indulging in another of my faults.' His mouth twisted derisively. 'I was being bloody arrogant again. Making love to you once, four years earlier, hardly seemed to justify that conceited assumption that Lowenna could be *my* child. . .maybe it was a psychological slip—because I *wanted* her to be mine so desperately? Just as much as I wanted *you* to be mine?'

She was drowning suddenly; drowning in the hypnotic gleam of his eyes. This was crazy, the calm, rational part of her brain was telling her. Madness. Letting Saul cleverly manipulate her emotions to get what he now appeared to want. . .letting him overwhelm her with his magnetism so that she ignored the glaringly obvious truth the past had taught her. . .

Mouth dry, heart pounding as if she'd just run a race, she stared at him uncomprehendingly.

'What about. . . Charmian?' It was a dogged persistence. 'She came to see me, when I was having a drink with Howard——'

'I could say, "What about Howard?"' Saul cut in softly, the pale eyes suddenly bright with aggression.

'Howard is a *friend*! I see him about—about once every six weeks, for a chat and a pub snack!' she retorted hotly. 'Charmian Baron has been sleeping at Leigh Barton with you, hasn't she? She told me you were going to marry her!'

Saul's response was terse and extremely coarse. 'Charmian has her own interior design company. I've been employing her, for heaven's sake!'

'Really? Then why should she have this strange little notion you're engaged to marry her, Saul?'

'Charmian has a very rich daddy,' he explained succinctly. 'She's used to getting her own way. I've known her, through her father, for some time. When she asked if she could help refurbish Leigh Barton, I thought she could be useful. I confess I've been too absorbed in other things to realise she had plans for a rosy future together.'

'But you must have been sleeping together?'

'We were not sleeping together.'

The flat coolness in Saul's voice made her fall silent.

'And, in case you're wondering, the ideas for colours and furnishings here are *my* choice—Charmian has merely done the spadework, the running around. . . To be truthful, I wanted a ready-made base here, something to show you that I meant to stay. . .something permanent and secure to offer you. . .'

There was a long, fraught pause. A log hissed and collapsed in the grate. Francesca finally stood up abruptly, pushing her chair back with such force that it overbalanced and clattered to the glossy wood-block floor. Her throat felt swollen with choked emotion.

'Saul. . . I *want* to believe this is all true. . . I want to believe in such a fantasy so much I'm *ashamed* of myself. . .but can't you see? It hurts too much! What happened between us that day years ago. . .it was a magical, tender moment for me, and then you broke it up and trampled on it and threw it back in my face! I just don't understand how you could have done that, and now come back and say you *love* me!'

She was white-faced, shaking. Saul stood up too, his dark face taut, his lidded eyes bleak.

'Chessy. . .listen, please listen to me. All my life I've felt I was trying to please different people, with different things. To please my stepfather I went to Eton and played polo; to please my mother I went to Oxford and studied Latin; to please my real father I lived and travelled with the gypsies, learned their customs and philosophies. At the end of the day, Chessy, I felt confused. When we met again at your eighteenth birthday party, I was having a minor identity crisis, as the saying goes. I suspect you were too. . .'

'I'm not sure I. . .' Her voice trailed off. Her heart was thumping faster than normal. Was it the wine? Or the hypnotic atmosphere Saul was creating with his clipped, intense monologue?

'I saw you that night at your birthday party, and I hated myself for wanting you. It felt like a betrayal. You looked so overjoyed to see me, and all I could think of was how much I wanted to take you to bed. I watched you flirting with all those young boyfriends, and I was so goddamned jealous I wanted to murder them. Your father took great pleasure in telling me you were engaged to marry Julian Harrington-Green.'

'But I *wasn't*. . .'

'No. . .' Saul expelled his breath sharply, closing his

eyes for a second '. . .you weren't. . .' He came round the table and took her hand in his, linking his fingers through hers, sending tremors of reaction all over her. 'Chessy, darling Chessy, when you came to see me the morning after your party, at the hotel, and we made love, it felt like a kind of brilliant wickedness—for all those reasons I've just given, and a few more. I felt as if I'd finally proved your father right—run true to form at last.' He squeezed her hand harder, his eyes darkening. 'I lashed out at you to save myself from going under. I couldn't believe I'd done it. That I'd broken a trust——'

'It wasn't like that; I wanted it too.' She whispered it so quietly that it hardly made a sound. 'It felt like a dream. . .like something I'd waited for forever. . .then suddenly you were like another person, you were so bitter and accusing.'

Saul's eyes held hers for a long moment. She felt as if she were drowning.

'I felt guilty as hell,' he said finally, his expression bleak. He released his grip on her hand, raking slightly shaky fingers through his dark hair. 'At the same time I was ripped apart with jealousy that I might not have been the first. . .lord, as if it really mattered! I was appalled at my own arrogance!'

'It mattered to me. And you were. . .' It was a low, shaky admission, the colour suddenly soaring high in her cheeks as the expression in Saul's eyes altered.

'So I'm beginning to realise,' he said softly, his own colour heightening slightly along his high cheekbones, reaching for her hand again as if he needed the contact, his thumb sliding over the pad of flesh below hers with a rhythmic caress.

'Chessy, it's hard to explain, I was going through a

kind of. . .*turmoil*. You'd been the one. . .*constant* in my life, the little step-cousin I'd always teased and played with. And then that changed too. Suddenly I wasn't sure how you saw me any longer. All those romantic stories of yours about gypsies. . . You seemed to live in a dream-world, completely detached from the reality of it.'

Her throat had dried completely. It was hard to speak. 'It's true I was. . .fascinated by your background,' she said slowly at last, 'and I used to love going to the horse fairs with you, and meeting the gypsies. It *did* seem terribly romantic, and exotic, and different. . .but it was *you* I loved, Saul, not some silly fantasy!'

Her use of the past tense brought a dark flicker of pain in his eyes. He dropped her hand and turned to lean against the chimneypiece, jerkily massaging his fingers through the dampness of his dark hair.

'Yes. I admit I was wrong. But my mother's marriage to my father was the *reality* of all the romantic gypsy nonsense, Chessy! Even I'd been guilty of illusions— *Boys Own* hero stuff—about my father. I didn't understand the reality until I started living with the gypsies. Then I could see the tragedy. I saw how my mother had succumbed to the romance of being the "gypsy's bride" and suffered the consequences. She loved my father, but Gallaghers always married Boswells, and when Jack Gallagher fell in love with my mother it was doomed to failure from the start. The clans closed ranks. Romanies tend to use marriage as a kind of political power-base. They inter-marry; a lot of first cousins marry. . . My mother threatened the security of two close-knit tribes. She never stood a chance.'

'But the same pressures would never have applied in our case!'

'No. . .but I was terrified you'd become infatuated for all the wrong reasons,' Saul confessed quietly, taking her hand between his and jolting her heart with the brilliant hardness of his gaze. 'And when your father claimed I was the equivalent to your "bit of rough", and that you'd rather die than get seriously involved with someone like me——'

'My father said *that*?' She snatched her hand away from him, staring at him, stunned. 'When? When did he say that?'

'When I went to see him, before I left.'

'I didn't know. . . You're saying you actually came to see my father? Told him what happened?' The blood had drained from her face.

'I came to see *you*,' Saul told her, his eyes hooded, 'later on that day. I couldn't just leave after all the abuse I'd hurled at you. After the way you'd rushed off in tears. I'd had a chance to cool down. But your father said you'd gone into Exeter with Julian Harrington-Green to choose an engagement ring. He said you'd then be attending a celebration soirée at the Harrington-Greens' that evening.'

Fists clenched at her sides, she stared into his eyes uncomprehendingly. The silence stretched on for so long that the ticking of the mantel clock seemed to grow louder and louder.

'But that's rubbish,' she said at last, realising that she was shaking all over with indignation, staring at Saul blindly. 'My father couldn't have said that! It's not true, Saul! I told him that morning, before I came to the hotel to see you—I told him I'd rather die than marry Julian. I went for a long ride when I'd left you!

That's where I was—out riding!' Tears had started from her eyes as she tried to absorb what Saul was telling her.

'Saul, you're *lying*!' she burst out on an angry sob, whirling on him in fury and lashing out at him, her fists catching him on the chest and the jaw before he caught her hands in a firm grip of steel, dragging her close against him, her wrists pinned behind her back. 'My father wouldn't have lied like that. . . Let go of me, Saul!'

'Francesca. . .stop it, stop fighting me. . .'

She was kicking wildly at his shins. Cursing under his breath, he swept her up and deposited her full length on the sofa, coming down on top of her, knocking the breath out of her, one long muscular thigh forcing her flailing legs into stillness.

'Stop it, you little hell-cat,' he murmured harshly. 'Do you think I'd lie to you about something like that?' Before she could retort he dropped his head and kissed her, hard and long on the mouth, taking full advantage of her parted lips to gain entry, his tongue delving hungrily inside, triggering an abrupt, mindless, anguished surrender. When he felt the tension leave her, he lifted his head again, his eyes darker with desire. She was crying, huge tears welling up and trickling down her temples towards her ears.

'Don't be angry with your father,' he said softly, seeing the silent misery of her eyes, cupping her fraught face in his hands, sliding his fingers into the damp tendrils of hair escaping her French plait. He rolled to one side of her, still holding her against him but no longer holding her prisoner. 'Your father had seen us together in the stable the night before, remember?' He went on gently, 'When I'd followed you out there, and found Neville Beresford had got there first with the handkerchief and sympathy? Your father had always seen me as a threat. Now the threat was becoming reality. He didn't know what had happened that morning in my hotel room. . .' Saul's eyes searched her face probingly. 'Unless you'd told him.'

'No——' she found her voice but it sounded as if it were coming from a long way away '—I didn't tell him anything until. . .until I couldn't hide my pregnancy any longer.' She sniffed, rubbing a shaky hand over her tear-stained face, and Saul levered himself up slightly, produced a clean white handkerchief from his back pocket with a wry flourish, and watched her scrub her face with it and then twist it absently between her hands. 'Then I had to tell him, or he'd have started suspecting one of my casual boyfriends, made scenes. . .' She shuddered, remembering. 'But when I admitted it was you he. . .he. . .' She bit her lip miserably. 'I made it clear I was never going to tell you and for once he didn't seem to want to argue!'

'Quite. An illegitimate grandchild was infinitely preferable to me for a son-in-law?' Saul nodded grimly.

'Oh, Saul. . .'

There was a long, resounding silence.

'In his way he was trying to protect you, Chessy,' Saul said at last, his voice harsh and slightly uneven, as if he was quelling his own anger. 'To him I was an undesirable rebel, a bad influence. He loved you very much, and he wanted to shield you from harm. I'm sorry he's dead, because if he'd lived I'd have forced him to see that he and I actually shared something in common—that same obsession with you. . .only I love you more than he could have begun to imagine. And I don't want to trap you and tie you down, Chessy. I want you to be free to grow as a person. . . I want an equal partner, my darling, not an obedient slave. . .'

Saul slid his hands down to her shoulders, caressing the rigid muscles of her arms as she stared up at him tensely.

'Saul. . .' She swallowed hard, a wave of dizziness suddenly washing over her. She was trembling all over, she realised. The intimacy of their position on the sofa was beginning to flood her whole body with a hectic warmth. 'Saul, I can't take this in properly. . .'

'Then you're not concentrating.' The light in his eyes was dazzling. With a slightly unsteady hand he smoothed her tousled hair back from her face, and kissed her lightly.

'Chessy, darling, if I could wipe out all that heart-ache, believe me I'd do it. But if you'll marry me now I promise you'll never have cause to regret it. . .*will* you marry me, Chessy?'

He was stroking her hot forehead as he spoke, his fingers sliding down her cheek to tilt her chin, raising her face for his inspection, his voice deceptively light and matter-of-fact, but there was a coiled-up tension in him, transmitting itself to her, and his eyes darkened fiercely as he read the answer in her eyes.

'Yes. . . I will.' Her voice was thick with tears, but she felt suddenly, disproportionately exultant. She smiled up at him so luminously he gave a low, rough groan, like that of a man whose life sentence had just been lifted.

'You will?'

She nodded wordlessly.

Pulling her hard against him, he crushed her hungrily against his chest, and for a while neither of them spoke. She could feel the dull thudding of his heart against hers. It made her feel vibrantly, joyfully alive, as if her blood were singing through her veins.

'Since you're the only person I've ever even considered marrying, I'd be mad to turn you down.' she whispered breathlessly, finally finding the ability to speak again, ensnared in the brilliant depths of his eyes, drinking in the sudden, blinding glory of it.

'Don't look at me like that. I'll forget all my earnest, noble intentions and then I won't be answerable for my actions. . .'

'What were your noble intentions?'

'To control my overwhelming desire to take you up to bed. I think we should wait until we're married now, don't you?'

'Well. . .'

Saul's eyes flickered as he read the kindling glow in hers. 'Besides, we haven't finished our meal. . .we haven't had the raspberries. . .' His eyes were moving devouringly over her mouth as she smiled up at him. 'Or the gâteau. . .'

'I don't think I could eat them now. . .'

'How about coffee?' His lips were tracing a warm, irresistible path along the soft base of her throat above the low wrap neckline of the blue and white dress, and heat was flaring out of control between them. The burgeoning arousal of his body made her writhe with shy longing beneath him.

'I couldn't drink coffee either. . .' She snaked her fingers convulsively through the dark thickness of his hair, her breath catching in her throat. 'Saul, when we were arguing after the polo match,' she said huskily, feeling his arms tighten possessively around her with a piercing stab of pleasure, 'and when I said I used to love you, but I didn't love you any more now. . .'

'Yes?' For an instant the hard body had frozen against her, his breathing shallow.

'I lied.'

Saul shuddered slightly. His grip tightened mercilessly.

'I've never been able to stop loving you, Saul, even though I've been trying for four years.'

'Chessy. . .' He kissed her fiercely, igniting the heat to a blaze which had little hope of being extinguished. 'Chessy, I want you so much, darling. . .'

'I want you too. . .' His weight was a savage sweetness as he moved across her, and she wrapped her arms round him passionately. 'Could we go to bed, Saul? Now?'

'I want my ring on your finger. . . I want to do things properly this time.' It was breathed thickly and without great conviction against her mouth as Saul found the fastening of the French plait and began to unravel the heavy strands of hair, threading his fingers through the shiny dark tresses until it tumbled wildly around her shoulders. He ran his hands possessively down over the thin, silky material of her dress, exploring each curve and hollow of her, sending her temperature soaring unbearably. 'I shouldn't be doing this,' he whispered softly. 'We should wait——'

'I *can't* wait.' It was a choked, breathless confession, half-laugh, half-sob. 'I've waited too long already!' To prove her point she smoothed impatient, trembling hands against the softness of his shirt, feeling the rigid muscles beneath, then tugged the material from the waistband of his cords and let her fingers begin a sensual investigation of their own.

Drawing back a fraction, he stared at her beneath lowered eyelids, his gaze ravenous on the slender figure beneath the spotted dress, moving from her bare, lightly tanned ankles up to the slim curve of thigh, then higher to the swell of her breasts visible at the neckline of her dress, the hard jut of her nipples clearly outlined.

'Bed it is, then.' He gave a shudder of laughing surrender. 'Bed is the only place I can do justice to you. . .'

It was dusk, and the big square bedroom with its stunning view across the Leigh Barton gardens was full of shadows, a soft colour-scheme of blue and grey and white counterpointed by the ancient blackened beams criss-crossing ceiling and walls.

Saul drew Francesca into his arms, his mouth searching for hers with mounting urgency; then she was lifted with impressive ease and laid flat on the bed. A sudden unexpected wave of shyness—almost apprehension—hit her as Saul began to slowly, lovingly undress her.

'Saul. . .' It was a shaky out-breath as she clung to his shoulders, battling with the slight wave of panic. 'Saul, I feel strange. . .'

'It's all right.' He kissed her deeply, drinking from the well of sweetness, smoothing his hands reassuringly over her body, and his sureness and confidence transformed all her fears into a kind of savage intensity. Heat engulfed her, sheening her skin with a damp slick of perspiration. She felt physically aware to such a heightened degree that it was as if every follicle of hair on her body prickled into awareness, each nerve-end quivering for Saul's hands to discover its location, placate its trembling impatience. . .

'I feel strange too.' There were buttons on the front of her dress, and with each button opened Saul's lips found a fresh triangle of silky skin. She clung to him fiercely, the dreamlike atmosphere in the room suddenly frightening her as if everything that had happened so far could be some cruel figment of her imagination.

'Tell me this is real,' she breathed softly. 'I'm afraid you'll vanish again. . . I'll wake up and find it's been a dream.'

'This is real.' There was husky amusement. The impedimentia of clothes was dealt with in a very undreamlike manner, and she was suddenly cooler, and exposed and vulnerable in the revealing ivory scraps of camisole and French knickers, the scanty lace hiding very little. 'I'm real. . .' Saul had hurled his clothes to the floor with shuddering haste, and he felt very real as his weight came down against her once more, the hair-roughened limbs and sensually smooth muscles making her feel faint with joyful desire, his skilful hands peeling the camisole upwards.

'You're so beautiful, Chessy.' The glittering hunger in his eyes as he stared at the soft, tawny curves of her bare flesh was almost as tantalising as the caresses of his fingers on her skin. She splayed her fingers longingly against his chest, exploring the powerful maleness of him, her teeth sinking into his hard shoulder as he slid the last silken scrap down over her thighs and followed the movement with his lips and his tongue.

'Saul. . .oh, Saul, love me now!' Her trembling wouldn't stop, the pleasure mounting higher and higher as she clutched him against her, opening to him, lifting herself to him, their coming together rapid and savage and totally unavoidable. She cried out as he burst into her, grinding her down on the soft quilt, filling her with his life-force, lips, mouths and bodies greedy for a

contact which was already as close as was physically
possible.

'Chessy. . .darling, darling Chessy. . .' It was a low
growl in his throat, and there was deep triumph in his
eyes, a glowing plundering triumph as he felt the
eruption of climax inside her, heard her strangled gasp,
watched the moments of total abandon as she trembled
and writhed beneath him. 'You're incredible. . .did
you know that?'

'I. . .' She was luminous, melting, floating, boneless
beneath him. 'Oh, Saul. . . I love you so much.'

They lay entwined for what seemed an eternity. The
bedroom grew completely dark, and eventually Saul
stirred sufficiently to click on a small bedside light and
prop himself on an elbow to look down into her face,
his hand stroking her wildly dishevelled hair where it
was spread out on the pillow. She shivered slightly and
he pulled the quilt over her, tucking it gently around
her as if she were made of precious porcelain.

'I didn't hurt you?' he whispered unevenly. 'I rather
lost control there. . .'

She shook her head slowly. It was a supreme effort
to speak, to rouse herself from the dark, sensual layers
of the aftermath of their lovemaking. Finally, she gazed
up into his eyes with a slight frown crinkling her
forehead, remembering that long-ago occasion in his
hotel room.

'You make me lose control too,' she whispered, glad
of the dim light to hide the colour warming her cheeks.
'I'd forgotten what it was like.'

Saul's eyes were quizzical suddenly. 'With me, you
mean?' he probed gently, the possessive light in his
eyes melting her bones. 'Or are you saying you haven't
done a great deal of this kind of thing for a while?'

Her colour was hectic now. 'I have to confess I haven't done any. . .' She blinked at the sudden fierce concentration in his gaze. 'The truth is, Saul, there's. . .there's only ever been you.'

He gathered her up against him, holding her tightly. His groan was softly remorseful against her hair.

'I definitely don't deserve this,' he murmured at last. 'You realise this will play havoc with my inflated ego?'

'I don't care. You wouldn't be the same without your ego! The thing is. . .' she hesitated slightly '. . .you were my first lover, yet it didn't—hurt at all.'

'I've thought about that since.' His voice held a throb of amusement suddenly. 'I think the explanation may lie in a combination of—how shall I put it?—extreme eagerness, and all that horse-riding?'

'Was I *too* eager, Saul?'

'You could never be that.'

She buried her hot face against his chest and felt him laugh softly. She ran her hands rapturously over the wonderful contours of his body, let her lips seek the tantalising taste and texture of his skin, the hard nub of his nipples among the coarse hair on his chest, shivering delicately as she aroused a clenched response in the hard arms encircling her. Then she turned on to her back, nestled in the warmth of his arm, staring up at the shadowy dark-beamed ceiling.

'I confess I wanted to kill Andrada today,' Saul murmured at last. 'Seeing you there with him, all eyes and legs in that skimpy little outfit, letting him kiss you——'

'I came with him because I was angry with you. Poor Gabriel; I must write him a letter, apologising.' Saul's arm tightened warningly around her, and she twisted her head up to look at his face. 'I used him to get back at you—that's a dreadful way to treat someone!'

'Not as dreadful as the way you've been treating me this last couple of weeks! I almost spent a night in Exeter Police Station thanks to your dreadful treatment of me!'

'I didn't feel terribly well-disposed towards your friend Charmian at the polo match,' she pointed out shakily. 'If I weren't such a well-brought-up girl I could easily have started a punch-up with her between chukkas!'

Saul laughed softly, and she wriggled closer, found his smiling mouth, and the kiss which followed ensured a lengthy silence.

'Will your mother be furious when she discovers Lowenna's really her grandchild?' she whispered at last.

'She'll be ecstatic. In fact I have the feeling she may have put two and two together long before I did!'

'I adore your mother. She's like the perfect example of a dream mother-in-law—quietly supportive and never interferes!'

'She seems fairly enchanted with you,' Saul's voice smiled into the darkness, 'so there's one potential source of marital conflict we'll avoid.

'Marital conflict?' she teased softly. 'That's very prosaic, since we haven't even had the wedding yet!'

'I'm a realist, Chessy. Real life isn't all red roses and champagne. . .'

'I didn't imagine it was!' she protested mildly. 'I'd only expect those once a week!'

'Sounds eminently reasonable!' It was a laughing growl against her hair before he kissed her at such length and with such thoroughness that she almost lost her chain of thought completely.

'What you were saying about fantasy and reality. . .' she began again, when she was freed for a moment '. . .about my having problems sorting one from the other? Seriously, you don't really think I live in a fantasy world, Saul?'

Abruptly, Saul twisted to haul her over on top of him, sending the temperature abruptly soaring between them all over again.

'I want us to share each other's world, Chessy. I want to be sure of a relationship which won't founder—as my mother's and father's did—because of false expectations.' He gave a low, husky laugh. 'Does that sound unrealistic?'

'Not at all,' she murmured softly, laughing down at him and writhing sensuously at the hardening contact of his body beneath hers. 'After all, I know how proud and jealous and arrogant and insecure you are—I don't think those are unrealistic expectations of my future husband?'

'Not really. . .' He gave her earlobe a warning nip and flipped her over to drag her submissively beneath him. 'Now, let's see,' he began with ominous softness, 'I expect you to love, honour and obey me forever, provide me with hordes more exact replicas of Lowenna, amalgamate Hill Mead Riding Stables with Leigh Barton Polo Training School, and steer well clear of Gabriel Andrada, Howard Graham, *et al*, as long as we both shall live. Are those unrealistic expectations of my future wife?'

'I don't *think* so. . .' She was breathless as the close body contact ignited desire. 'In fact, I'd say you've got the realities of the situation pretty well taped——'

Abruptly the banter ceased, and the loving started all over again. By mutual accord fantasy and reality at last merged and blurred and melted quite acceptably into one.

Next month's Romances

Each month, you can choose from a world of variety in romance with Mills & Boon. These are the new titles to look out for next month.

DANGEROUS INTERLOPER Penny Jordan

BETRAYED Anne Mather

TEMPT ME NOT Susan Napier

FORBIDDEN ENCHANTMENT Patricia Wilson

STAY UNTIL DAWN Elizabeth Oldfield

LASTING LEGACY Kay Thorpe

FORBIDDEN PASSION Sarah Holland

OUTBACK MAN Miranda Lee

MAN OF TRUTH Jessica Marchant

CARIBBEAN DESIRE Cathy Williams

SHADOW IN THE WINGS Lee Stafford

RISK OF THE HEART Grace Green

THE PARIS TYPE Christine Greig

HEARTSONG Melinda Cross

THE OTHER WOMAN Jessica Steele

STARSIGN
FORTUNE IN THE STARS Kate Proctor

Mills & Boon

Do you long to escape to romantic, exotic places?

To a different world – a world of romance?

THE PAGES OF A MILLS & BOON WILL TAKE YOU THERE

Look out for the special Romances with the FARAWAY PLACES stamp on the front cover, and you're guaranteed to escape to distant shores, to share the lives and loves of heroes and heroines set against backgrounds of faraway, exotic locations.

There will be one of these special Romances every month for 12 months. The first is set on the beautiful island of Tobago in the Caribbean.

Available from September, 1991 at:

Boots, Martins, John Menzies, W.H. Smith, Woolworths and other paperback stockists.

Also available from Mills and Boon Reader Service, P.O. Box 236, Thornton Road, Croydon, Surrey CR9 3RU.

4 FREE

Romances
and 2 FREE gifts
just for you!

*You can enjoy all the
heartwarming emotion of true love for FREE!
Discover the heartbreak and the happiness, the emotion
and the tenderness of the modern relationships in
Mills & Boon Romances.*

*We'll send you 4 captivating Romances as a special offer
from Mills & Boon Reader Service, along with the chance to
have 6 Romances delivered to your door each month.*

Claim your FREE books and gifts overleaf...

An irresistible offer from Mills & Boon

Here's a personal invitation from Mills & Boon Reader Service, to become a regular reader of Romances. To welcome you, we'd like you to have 4 books, a CUDDLY TEDDY and a special MYSTERY GIFT absolutely FREE.

Then you could look forward each month to receiving 6 brand new Romances, delivered to your door, postage and packing free! Plus our free newsletter featuring author news, competitions, special offers and much more.

This invitation comes with no strings attached. You may cancel or suspend your subscription at any time, and still keep your free books and gifts.

It's so easy. Send no money now. Simply fill in the coupon below and post it to -

Reader Service, FREEPOST, PO Box 236, Croydon, Surrey CR9 9EL.

Free Books Coupon

Yes! Please rush me my 4 free Romances and 2 free gifts! Please also reserve me a Reader Service subscription. If I decide to subscribe I can look forward to receiving 6 brand new Romances each month for just £9.60, postage and packing free. If I choose not to subscribe I shall write to you within 10 days - I can keep the books and gifts whatever I decide. I may cancel or suspend my subscription at any time. I am over 18 years of age.

Name Mrs/Miss/Ms/Mr _____ EP18R

Address _____

_____

Postcode _____ Signature _____

Offer expires 31st May 1992. The right is reserved to refuse an application and change the terms of this offer. Readers overseas and in Eire please send for details. Southern Africa write to Independant Book Services, Postbag X3010, Randburg 2125.
You may be mailed with offers from other reputable companies as a result of this application.
If you would prefer not to share in this opportunity, please tick box ☐

mps
MAILING
PREFERENCE
SERVICE